P9-DGP-165

Dynamics of Response

Dynamics of Response

Joseph M. Notterman
Princeton University

Donald E. Mintz
City College of the City University of New York

John Wiley & Sons, Inc. New York · London · Sydney

Library of Congress Catalog Card Number: 65-24294
Printed in the United States of America

For Becky, Danny, and Abby
JMN

For Peter
DEM

Preface

PROGRAMMATIC SUPPORT of research permits, but does not insure, the gradual development of experimental technique, the corroboration of puzzling findings, and the eventual emergence of data-anchored theories. These favorable aspects of long-range research activity are maximized if the investigator is afforded the opportunity of publishing his work as a whole, rather than piecemeal. The reasons are fairly obvious: first, the researcher is compelled to compare the logic underlying the interpretation of findings reported in one chapter with those appearing in another, and inconsistencies must be identified and—where possible—constructively eliminated; second, because of the greater variety of experimental situations examined, the likelihood of generalizations being discovered is enhanced; and third, because of deliberate attempts at synthesis, the existence of gaps in knowledge or understanding is more readily made apparent.

Accordingly, it is our good fortune to have had the opportunity to publish the results of our research program in this single, overall account. Nonetheless, the reader will quickly recognize that despite our best efforts to the contrary, there remain many valid questions of approach, of "fact," and of interpretation. Perhaps this is as it should be, for who can pretend completeness in any analysis of behavior?

J. M. N.
D. E. M.

Acknowledgments

IT IS WITH PLEASURE and gratitude that we acknowledge our debt to the following people. First, we are obligated to Richard Trumbull and Gilbert Tolhurst of the Office of Naval Research for expressions of confidence over the years. Second, we thank the several graduate research assistants who were closely associated with our research program: A. H. Block, I. Goldberg, R. D. L. Filion, M. Leffand, F. J. Mandriota, T. Marton, and M. A. Morfield. Third, we express appreciation to the group of nonacademic research aides and typists who ran subjects, punched cards, processed data, prepared copy, and—in general—made laboratory life worth living: Ann Cox, Nora Kim, Anita Lee Mixson, and Zinta Sovers. Fourth, we are most grateful to the engineers and computer experts without whom the data gathering and analysis would have been impossible: D. Brown, R. Bueller, N. Marple, and A. F. Sciorra. To Mr. Sciorra we owe a special debt for his faithful diligence over the long period of time during which he has served as engineering consultant. Fifth, to J. A. Dinsmoor we extend thanks for his critical review of the prepublication manuscript. And finally we are indebted to Jeanette F. Koffler who, although nominally a nonacademic research aide, was actually personnel expert, laboratory supervisor, manuscript coordinator, and general handholder during the entire effort culminating in this book.

The research reported in this book was supported by Contract NONR-1858(19) between the Office of Naval Research and Princeton University.

JOSEPH M. NOTTERMAN
Princeton University

DONALD E. MINTZ
City College of the City
University of New York

Contents

Chapter One

Rationale

DEFINING A "RESPONSE," like many other fundamental matters, touches upon basic assumptions that may differ from scientist to scientist. We accept the deterministic view that a response is an identifiable change in behavior, one that is always the consequence of a prior event called the "stimulus." If a response is observed, a stimulus must have preceded it, whether or not the scientist can identify this initiating event.

There are qualifications in the stimulus-response relationship, however, which present limitations on the one hand, and on the other, increased generality. Although a stimulus is a *necessary* precursor of a response, it is not always *sufficient*. The traditionally accepted distinction between operant and respondent behavior rests primarily upon the sufficiency of the controlling stimulus. "Conditioned" behavior, operant or respondent, by its very definition implies a set of qualifications imposed upon the stimulus-response relationship. The interaction of such factors as physiological state of the organism, presence of other stimuli, other ongoing behavior, prior reinforcement history, particular neurological subsystem energized, and so on, may represent an additional set of necessary conditions. In most reports of behavioral research, unfortunately including the present account, some of these factors are ignored, others are hopefully held "constant," and still others are treated as experimental parameters. The event termed "stimulus" by the experimenter is usually a conveniently isolatable factor, which is only one of the several that must be present (that is, are "necessary") for a change in behavior to be recorded. In fact, it is only by *ad hoc* reasoning that after observing the occurrence of a response, the experimenter is able to say that

1

not only have the necessary conditions (or values) been met, but the sufficient as well.

From the foregoing comment, we trust it is clear that, like most other modern behaviorists, we recognize a distinction between the mechanistic, physiological concept of stimulus-response reflex and the descriptive, psychological concept. We believe that each of these views represents an anchor point at an opposite end of a continuum. The mechanistic approach successfully handles stimulus-response correlations of a frankly physiological character: those in which a specific stimulus regularly elicits a specific response without the need for any training and thus superficially, at least, appears to be sufficient as well as necessary. The psychological concept deals with stimulus-response correlations that have to be established by training procedures: those in which the stimulus initially is neither necessary nor sufficient as the antecedent of a specific response.

Response Specification and Measurement. To say that a response is a "change in behavior" places importance on the distinction between "no change" and "change." Consider the examination of bar-pressing behavior: by means of appropriate recording equipment, we determine that a response has been made; this information is obtained with no apparent lack of decisiveness or precision. But when has the condition of the organism passed from that of "no change" to that of "change" and then back again to "no change"? Obviously, we are dependent on the elastic constant of a spring within a microswitch to resolve whatever doubt may exist. Whenever the spring has been compressed sufficiently for a pair of contacts to pass from open to closed and subsequently from closed to open, the cycle of no change to change and back again has been completed, and a response emitted.

By changing the tensile quality of the spring, we may increase or decrease the level of force that, by these mechanical operations, comes to define a "response."

This type of response specification is on an "occurrence" basis and is used principally in situations that raise the experimental question, "How many responses will an organism make after exposure to such-and-such conditions?"

Skinner, the progenitor of the bar-pressing situation, has made clear, however, that this datum is *not* the one of paramount interest to him. It is rather the interval between responses (or, inversely, frequency of responses) that provides the fundamental information of value to the experimenter. He said:

. . . the main datum to be measured in the study of the dynamic laws of
an operant is the length of time elapsing between a response and the response immediately preceding it or, in other words, the rate of responding
(Skinner, 1938, p. 58).

In terms of response specification and measurement, it is apparent,
then, that the usual Skinnerian situation is characterized by (1) a
response defined in terms of the minimal force required to close a
microswitch but registered on an "occurrence" basis, without reference
to the actual level of suprathreshold force emitted; (2) a dependent
variable that may be expressed either as time intervening between
responses or as number of responses per unit of time.

But what of the dimensional properties of the response itself? Every
bar-pressing response must consist of a finite variation of force emitted
over a finite duration. In the usual bar-pressing experiment, the only
information we have concerning the response per se is that it exceeded
a minimal force level. We do not know by how much and we do not
know for how long—but we might not care to know! After all, there
is much to be said for not collecting information merely because it
is available, if such information is of little or no interest to the experimenter.

There precisely lies the problem: are there significant experimental
or theoretical questions best answered by examination of the dimensional characteristics of the response itself rather than by study of
the time interval between responses?

It is the over-all objective of this account to propose that the foregoing query must be answered in the affirmative. Evidence will be
produced showing that there are, indeed, fundamental theoretical and
experimental issues bearing upon schedules of reinforcement, drive
operations, rate of expenditure of effort, serial effects, differentiation
and discrimination, response-induced exteroceptive and proprioceptive
feedback, reactive inhibition, and so on, that demand more information than is provided by "time–between–occurrence" measures.

The concept of "reflex strength" in operant conditioning is based
often upon such response frequency measures. It is our intention to
demonstrate that experimental operations affecting reflex strength
may concurrently generate considerable change in the dimensional
characteristics of the response. Measures of behavioral variability and
the relationship between the criteria for reinforcement and the response populations that they generate are among the data that may
be no less fundamental to the dynamic laws of the operant than rate

of response. We must ask not only "what rate?" but also "rate of what?" Within the operationally defined generic class of the "occurrence" type of response, readily identifiable dimensional subclasses exist. The relative frequencies of these may provide a vital analytic complement to the absolute frequency of response.

But before describing the several experiments bearing upon these issues, which we and others have performed, we must examine carefully the physical and biological nature of force, work, energy, and other variables of interest.

Operational Properties of the Bar-Pressing Response. There is a striking parallel between the defining operations of "force" in physics and "operant" in psychology. The former is defined in terms of its effect upon the state of rest or motion of matter (Hodgman, 1943). Whenever the state of rest or motion of an object changes, the presence of an unbalancing force is inferred. The "operant," as we have seen, is defined in terms of the effect of motor behavior upon some specific object in the environment. In the Skinner box, for example, this takes the form of depressing the lever. If the normal state of rest of the lever is disturbed, and if the disturbance results in a large enough lever displacement or spring compression, a "response" is recorded. But, as just noted, the state of rest of an object cannot be changed unless some force has been exerted. Hence, it is possible to redefine operant behavior as behavior *that is tantamount to the organismic emission of forces.*

This concept of the operational definition of operant behavior is actually not so radical as may appear at first glance. It is implicit in each of the three major prototypes of instrumental responding—problem solving, lever pressing, and runway locomotion. What distinguishes these techniques is not the presence or absence of a force requirement—it is always present—but rather the experimental environment or the measurement procedure used to observe the effects of force emission. With lever pressing, the sensing device is a make-break switch; in the runway instance, it is the observed speed of the organism as it exerts force against the runway floor; in the Thorndikian situation, it is the sequence of movements resulting from the correct temporal and spatial application of force.

Returning to the main thread of the argument, we are asserting that operant behavior may be defined as the emission of mechanical forces by a living organism. We are not asserting that because of this, the only or the best way of describing acquired motor behavior is through the measurement of the force of responses. Although force emission constitutes the basic motor output of the animal organism (as contrasted, for example, to duration or displacement of response, or time between responses), it does not necessarily follow that measurement of force per se uniformly provides the scientist with the most useful source of information in any given experiment. We hope, however, that the program of research we are here reporting will aid in the formulation of those principles whereby the scientist can make a rational decision as to which descriptive system is most suitable for a specific class of experimental questions.

Relations among Force, Work, and Energy. One of the immediate consequences of conceiving of force as being the basic output of the organism is the raising of several significant questions concerning the influence of energy expenditure upon behavior. The theorist most concerned with these issues is, of course, Hull (1943), whose emphasis upon the explanatory importance of "reactive inhibition" makes it central to his theoretical formulations. Solomon (1948) has observed that the logical construct of "reactive inhibition" has had its empirical influence upon studies that he classifies in the following four types: the Law of Least Effort; effort per unit of time in conditioning and learning; avoidance of repetition of responses; and the role of kinesthesis in control of behavior. Solomon's scholarly review of the various experiments in these categories is extremely valuable for the systematization it provides.

A more recent contribution to this literature by Trotter (1956) emphasizes the need for clearer specification of the physical variables involved. He comments on the "vague" use by psychologists of terms such as work, energy, and force. Our examination of the relevant literature satisfies us that Trotter's contention is correct. Since several of the experiments described in the present account bear upon the general relation of energy expenditure to behavior, a preliminary discussion of the pertinent variables seems to be in order.

Everyone is familiar with the apparent paradox of becoming exhausted by pushing with all of one's strength against some immovable object without having performed any work in the accepted physical sense of the term. Work is accomplished only when the point of application of a force is displaced some finite distance (work = force × distance). Why then does the person pushing against a wall become exhausted? For two reasons: a certain amount of energy does go into the work initially necessary to stretch and to contract muscle groups;

simultaneously and subsequently, energy conversions occur, which constitute irreversible transformations, representing a biological "consumption" or "waste" of the total energy available to the organism. Thus, much of the energy of our hypothetical organism is converted metabolically to heat, which is then dissipated into the environment.

Along these lines, consider a rat that is pressing a bar and then "holding" (that is, keeping it depressed). In moving the lever through its full excursion the animal is exerting a force through a distance and is, therefore, doing work. In keeping the bar depressed the animal is not doing any more work, although—since muscle groups are being maintained in a state of extension and flection—the rat is metabolically converting energy from the body stores to heat.

This particular example emphasizes that, despite the dimensional identification of work with energy, there are many significant behavioral situations in which the empirical measurement of work accomplished in the environment will not be indicative of the energy released by the organism.

To recapitulate, energy is the capability of doing work, and work is the exertion of a force through a distance. But we cannot simply observe the work done by an organism and assume that we have accounted for all the energy "expended" (converted from a form usable to a form nonusable by the organism). Bearing in mind the law of nature that energy can neither be created nor destroyed, one must recognize that the following major energy transformations are involved

ORGANISM POTENTIAL ENERGY →

$$\text{WORK} \qquad + \text{ METABOLIC HEAT ENERGY} \qquad (1)$$
$$\text{(Kinetic Energy} \rightarrow \text{Potential Energy)}$$

As Kleiner (1948) stated: "Muscular work is accomplished by the body at the expense of increased metabolism. The potential energy of the foodstuff is transformed into the free energy of work and the energy of heat" (p. 498). The expression to the left of equation 1 is intended to represent only the portion of the energy available to the organism that can be directed to muscular activity. Energy dissipated in routine basal metabolism may be understood as a continuously present parameter.

If force is exerted, and the point of application of the force is not displaced, the consequence of the force is not work but—through the chemistry of metabolism involved in maintaining muscle tonus—more and more heat energy. It remains, nevertheless, that both terms of the right-hand side of equation 1 are contingent on the generation of motor behavior, that is, the exertion of force. Or

$$\text{WORK} + \text{METABOLIC HEAT ENERGY} = f(\text{FORCE}) \qquad (2)$$

What we have shown in the foregoing paradigm is a "total" or "final product" relationship. In actuality, the relationship is based on the rates of energy utilization and conversion (or "power") and the duration of these rates. The average power form is

$$\text{ORGANISM } P.E. \rightarrow \frac{\text{work}}{\text{time}} \times \text{duration} + \frac{\text{heat}}{\text{time}} \times \text{duration} \qquad (3)$$

in which both work/time and heat/time are expressions of "average power."

Combining the right-hand side of equation 3 and expressing the relationship in integral form, we have

$$\text{ORGANISM } P.E. = \int \text{POWER } dt$$

And as with equation 2, since the time integral of power depends upon the time integral of force exertion,

$$\int \text{POWER } dt = f\left(\int \text{FORCE } dt\right)$$

In short, and as Trotter (1956) has noted, the best index of energy expenditure during motor behavior is the time integral of force of response, a dimension we henceforth refer to as "effort." [1] It is *not* work or the product of force and distance.

The force exertion discussed here is specifically manipulandum-oriented, representing the forces emitted in executing the selected response. Nonmanipulandum-oriented activity remains an unmeasured component that presumably varies inversely with the rate of response and accounts for the expenditure of additional organism energy. Its exclusion from measurement appears justified by the over-all purpose of an analysis of operant behavior—a formulation of the relationship between the dependent variable (response) and the parameters defined by the experimental operations. With a lever-press response taken as the basis for reinforcement contingencies, the time integral of force of that response remains the appropriate index of organism energy expenditure.

[1] The physicist defines $\int F\, dt$ as "impulse," a term that has been pre-empted by the psychologist for other purposes.

However, in those behavioral situations in which "holding" behavior is infrequent (that is, emitted force reaches its peak value and then decreases rapidly to zero) and in which the work done by the organism goes into compressing or stretching a spring or strain gauge, peak force of response should be a satisfactorily valid index of energy utilization. It seems reasonable to assume that this follows from equation 2, since (1) as long as force is increasing to its peak value and is also within the elastic limit of the manipulandum, there must be increasing displacement at the point of application of the force (Hooke's Law), and the organism's energy is, therefore, going into work and the correlative metabolic heat loss; and (2) in the ideal spring or strain gauge, force and displacement covary, and work is, therefore, entirely predicted from the peak amplitude of the force alone. Accordingly, major analytic attention is given to the peak force of response in the research reported in this volume.

Chapter Two

Apparatus and General Procedure

THE BASIC APPARATUS involved in the series of experiments reported in this volume differs from the more traditional operant-conditioning apparatus in several important respects. Most of these relate to the types of measurements made. Each individual response provides a number of dimensional measures in addition to the "occurrence" measures typically taken on cumulative recording and impulse counters. This quantification of response dimensions provides a basis on which reinforcement contingencies may be established.

The apparatus details described in this chapter are intended to provide an abstract of the system's functions. Specifics have been included only where they would contribute to an understanding of operational limitations or experimental parameters. Detailed circuit diagrams and component specifications have generally been omitted since current electronic technology would allow for numerous improvements.

Figure 2-1 presents a block diagram of the entire system with the major components indicated. Two primary functions are involved and will be separately traced. They are (1) instrumentation of the experimental parameters and (2) recording of the data.

Instrumentation of the Experimental Parameters

The initial component of the entire system is the manipulandum, a strain-gauge bar. This is affixed to one wall of the experimental cage. The portion available to the animal inside of the cage is a brass ball $\frac{1}{2}$ in. in diameter flattened on the top to provide a horizontal plane approximately $\frac{7}{16}$ in. in diameter. The ball is tangential to a slight

9

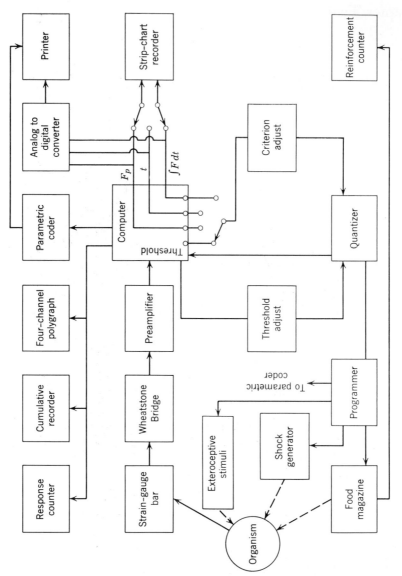

Figure 2-1 Block diagram of system.

recess in the cage wall and is surrounded at its lower half by a stainless steel guard designed to limit the subject's contact to the flattened top of the ball. The mechanics of the manipulandum are such that the usual displacement is extremely small. A 100-gm. force results in an excursion of the point of contact of less than $\frac{1}{32}$ in. The variations permitted in the locus of the point of contact of the manipulandum have purposely been kept small relative to the length of the lever arm to insure that variations in the moment of force reflect force and not length changes. A photograph of the cage, manipulandum, and pellet tray is shown in Fig. 2-2.

Force applied to the ball is mechanically transmitted to bonded strain gauges at the base of the lever. The strain gauges constitute a component of the Wheatstone Bridge (Fig. 2-1). Voltage from the Wheatstone Bridge is balanced to zero with no force applied to the manipulandum. The voltage increases as a linear function of the

Figure 2-2 Photograph showing top view of experimental test chamber. Water bottle is on left, rat lever in center, and pellet tray on right rear wall of cage.

stretch of the strain gauges, which, in turn, is linear with the applied force on the ball (Hooke's Law). Note that the problem of specification of the force involved in the acceleration of a mass (i.e., $F = ma$) has been minimized because of the fairly trivial excursion of the manipulandum. It is for this reason that Hooke's Law (which does not, of course, contain any velocity or acceleration terms) may be assumed to account almost entirely for the effects of the force applied to the ball. The maximum load capacity of the strain gauges is well in excess of the 272-gm. limit on force imposed by other components of the system.

A preamplifier increases the voltage from the Wheatstone Bridge and provides the input to the Analog Computer. Further amplification is accomplished at the Computer where one channel provides a continuous voltage analog of the force at the manipulandum. This force channel is fed to the Quantizer through the Threshold Adjust, an amplifier and potentiometer for setting the voltage level selected to define a response. When the selected level is reached, the Quantizer sets the Computer in "operate." When the voltage falls below the pre-established threshold value, the Quantizer switches the Computer through a "cycle" period into a nonoperate stage, and it is ready to repeat this sequence.

The period of time the Computer is in "operate" corresponds to the duration of a response and is analogous to the period of contact closure on the conventional microswitch manipulandum. During the operate period the Computer performs the following three quantification functions:

1. A constant voltage is integrated resulting in a linear ramp whose terminal value is a voltage analog of the response duration (t).

2. The time-variant voltage from the strain gauge is integrated. This identifies the time integral of force ($\int F\,dt$).

3. The maximum voltage from the strain gauge is retained providing a voltage analog of peak force (F_p).

An additional function of the Quantizer is the storing of pulses to perform various response-contingent operations (typically, reinforcement or step advances in ratio schedules). During the course of a response the Quantizer will "count up," and during the "cycle" period immediately following termination of a response will "count down" in the form of electrical pulses the number of "count-up" steps of the response. An arbitrary limit to the number of counts per response may be set. The Quantizer count may be based on any of the three response dimensions (F_p, t, $\int F\,dt$), or it may be based simply on the achievement of response threshold causing every response to produce the full number of output pulses set by the arbitrary limit.

When the Quantizer counting is based on a response dimension, the Criterion Adjust provides a means for calibrating the count scale. For example, a duration criterion might be selected and calibrated so that there is one count for each 0.1 second of response duration. Further, a limit for the maximum number of counts might be imposed. At the end of the response the Quantizer output is fed to the Programmer.

Many functions of the Programmer are similar to well-known techniques employed in schedules of reinforcement and discrimination training and do not need explanation. Most functions peculiar to the present apparatus are dependent on a response dimension. For these, appropriate relay circuitry is involved in establishing stimulus contingencies dependent on the pulse output of the Quantizer, that is, behavior-correlated contingencies.

The Programmer, in conjunction with the Quantizer, establishes the input to the Food Magazine, S^D Source, and Shock Generator, which directly perform the stimulus operations involved in the particular experimental design. Nonbehavior-correlated contingencies are instrumented through the usual techniques employing timers.

Recording of Data

The data-recording components of the experimental system receive information primarily from the Computer. Reinforcement and response counters, a Cumulative Recorder, and a Four-Channel Polygraph may all be used to collect "occurrence" information in a manner comparable with traditional operant apparatus. A graphic analog record of the response dimensions is maintained by the Strip Chart Recorder. A sample of such a record is shown in Fig. 2-3. The three measures (force, duration, and $\int F\,dt$) can be recorded concurrently: force from the continuous output of the Computer force channel, which at every instant has a voltage proportional to force at the manipulandum; $\int F\,dt$ as a cumulative displacement along the ordinate during the period of a response; and duration as distance along the abscissa.

A printed tape record of the values of the response dimensions is also maintained and provides the basis for most of the data reduc-

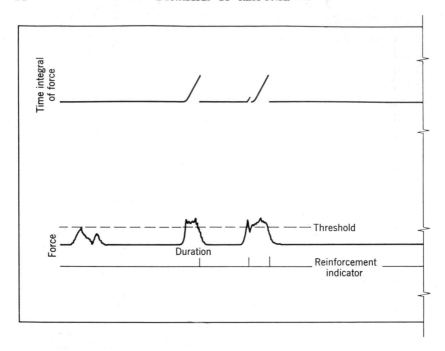

Figure 2-3 Sample Sanborn strip-chart record. In the lower portion of the record the dotted "Threshold" line has been added to indicate the force level that must be reached in order for the event to be considered a response. (After Notterman, 1959.)

tion reported. The major units in this recording component are three Hewlett-Packard 405 AR Digital Voltmeters (analog to digital converters), and a Hewlett-Packard 561B Printer. During the "cycle" period immediately following a response, the voltage analogs of peak force, response duration, and $\int F \, dt$ are sensed by the Voltmeters, which in turn position the Printer wheels, giving a three-digit measure of each dimension. The Parametric Coder positions one Printer wheel directly during this period. Inputs to the Parametric Coder from the Programmer and Computer provide the basis for a digital coding of three binary bits. The parameters coded varied with the experimental operations but typically involved events such as reinforcement, meeting of criterion, presentation of discriminative stimuli, and reinforcement eligibility in schedules. This coding greatly facilitated the data analysis of response subclasses defined by a variety of parameters.

Measurement Limits and Characteristics

Certain arbitrary limits, discretionary parameters, and restrictions imposed by the nature of the apparatus and data-collection techniques require mention.

Peak force was measured in 1-gm. intervals from threshold to 272 gm., the upper limit imposed by amplifier saturation in the Computer. A calibration curve of the strain-gauge manipulandum is shown in Fig. 2-4. This was obtained by applying weights to the manipulandum and reading the voltage at the Computer force channel. Linearity is evident over this dynamic range and has been verified for the entire range of the system.

Duration (t) and effort ($\int F\,dt$) were measured from 0 to 9.99 seconds in 0.01-second intervals, and 0 to 99.9-gram-seconds in 0.1-gram-second intervals respectively. Values above the upper limit were rare, and those that did occur were arbitrarily placed at the limiting value. Periodic validation checks of peak force and duration produced errors of less than 5 per cent, and less than ±0.1 gram-second for $\int F\,dt$ over most of the range of interest.

A limiting interresponse time (IRT) of 240 to 330 milliseconds existed, varying with the nature of the response-contingent operations

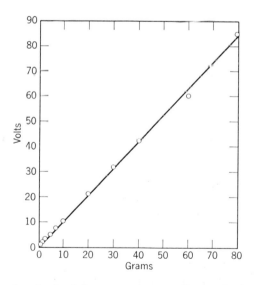

Figure 2-4   Linearity check of force transducer; voltage output as a function of weight of force (in grams) on lever. (After Notterman, 1959.)

involved but constant for any single experiment. Essentially, the IRT limit was a "dead" time during which the apparatus was insensitive to behavior at the manipulandum. This dead time commenced at the instant of response termination.

The response-threshold value for F_p of 2.5 gm. was selected on a basis of exploratory investigations with pilot animals. Values as low as 0.3 gm. were employed, resulting in a bimodal distribution of peak forces apparently attributable to two distinct topographical classes of organism-manipulandum contact. The plethora of extremely low-force "response" (less than 1 gm.) was the result of organism contact at varied points such as the tail, whiskers, body fur, etc. On the other hand, paw presses rarely fell within this range. A level of 2.5 gm. is high enough to filter out a wide variety of topographical variants and yet is low enough to exclude very few paw presses. The guard around the manipulandum also contributed to this end. The differentiation of response topography contingent upon this or any other operational definition of response is invariably arbitrary. The choice of values that would produce relatively high topographical homogeneity was considered essential to the program of experimentation, in which a major objective was to make comparisons of response dimensions where other aspects of the response were constant. For instance, a change in peak force that corresponds to a change from body brushing of the bar to paw pressing is different in kind from a change in the force of paw pressing. Nevertheless, the operations involved in response definition are indifferent to such a distinction, and the restriction can only be imposed by the choice of defining parameters and by the engineering of the physical characteristics of the manipulandum.

Maintaining the response threshold distinct from the reinforcement criterion was a further procedure dictated by the nature of the experimentation. "Response" remains a behavior-sampling unit, the basic datum in a behavior study. Not all members of this class need be eligible for reinforcement. The criterion defines the reinforcement-eligible subclass of response. The alternative to this is to have the response definition correspond to reinforcement eligibility; then a criterion change results in a different sampling procedure, a different physical response definition. Comparisons of data from different reinforcement criteria would thus suffer from the confounding of the reinforcement criterion with the response definition. To make sensible statements concerning the effects of various reinforcement contingencies it appears essential to maintain the distinction between the contingency and the sampling unit.

Response Dimensions, Threshold, and Criterion

Figure 2-5 shows a schematic representation of the force-time function as it might be recorded on the Strip Chart Recorder from the force channel of the Computer. The horizontal base line corresponds to zero force at the manipulandum.

Response threshold is indicated by the 2.5-gm. line. As the defining limit of a response it provides the basis for data sampling and experimental contingency operations. The peak marked A and the two at C and D all represent responses. B is a force output with a maximum below threshold and consequently is not a response as here defined. Two separate responses exist at C and D, even though the force output did not return to zero.

Peak force (F_p) is the maximum force reached during a response as measured from the baseline. Duration (t) is simply the elapsed time between the ascending and descending threshold crossings. The area under the curve during the temporal limits of a response corresponds to the $\int F\,dt$. In addition to the foregoing, average force $(\overline{F})$ is involved in the discussion of some experiments. This quantity may be described as the height of the square-wave equivalent of a given response and is mathematically stated as $\dfrac{\int F\,dt}{t}$.

The criterion for reinforcement or any response-contingent operation may be determined by a particular value of the peak force, duration, or time integral of force of response. In effect, this establishes a

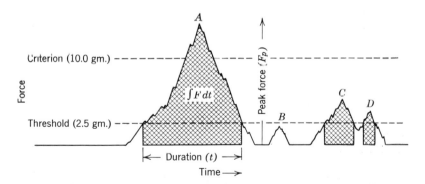

Figure 2-5 Schematic representation of a force-time record showing the peak force, duration, and time integral of force of response. A, C, and D are all responses; B is not a response as the force level did not reach the 2.5-gm. response threshold. Only the response A has reached the reinforcement criterion depicted, 10-gm. peak force.

quantitatively defined response subclass. Illustrated in Fig. 2-5 is a 10-gm. F_p criterion in which only the response A has met this value. "Band criteria" may also be established, requiring a maximum as well as a minimum value to define the response subclass (see Chapter 5).

Response Units

The response dimensions reported belong to the usual class of centimeter-gram-second units. Durations are specified in seconds; force is stated in grams rather than the absolute units, dynes. Under the standard value of the gravitational constant ($g = 980.665$ cm./sec.^{2}) adopted by the International Committee on Weights and Measures, a weight of 1 gm. is equivalent to a force of 980.665 dynes. This value provides the appropriate conversion factor. In practice, manipulandum calibration was accomplished through the application of known weights at point of contact on the lever.

Gram-second, the gravitational equivalent of dyne-second, is the unit of measurement for $\int F\, dt$. The aforementioned conversion factor is again appropriate.

General Procedure

Certain general procedural conditions prevailed throughout the course of the experimentation. Exceptions are noted in the descriptions of the specific experiments in which they occurred.

Subjects. The subjects in all experiments were male albino rats of the Wistar strain, obtained from the Charles River Breeding Laboratory. Each was between 200 and 350 gm. in weight and between 90 and 120 days of age when received (60-day-old animals were used for avoidance conditioning—Chapter 12). Purina laboratory mash was used for home cage feeding, and Noyes 45-mg. pellets were employed as standard experimental reinforcement unless 20-mg. pellets are specifically indicated. A standard 23-hour food deprivation regimen with a one-hour feeding period was established for the entire colony, and animals were maintained on this procedure for 10 to 40 days before their initial introduction into the experimental environment.

Experimental Environment. The experimental cage, pellet magazine, and necessary stimulus display equipment were housed in a sound-insulated experimental room. Semidarkness was maintained during a run session; the only illumination was provided by a frosted white 7½-watt indirect lamp located approximately 2½ ft. from the experimental cage. An electric fan was kept running to facilitate ventilation and temperature uniformity and to enhance sound masking. Air conditioning and heating were employed to maintain uniform temperature and humidity.

A noteworthy deviation from the usual operant-conditioning apparatus was the silent operation of the manipulandum. Unlike the microswitch of conventional manipulanda, the strain-gauge lever provided no audible correlate of the beginning and end of the response. The only behavior-correlated sound available to the organism was the food-magazine operation, and this only occurred following the termination of a response that met the reinforcement criterion.

Fresh water was continuously available within the home and experimental cages.

Run Procedure. Animals were run after an approximately 23-hour food deprivation. The free-feeding hour in the home cage was given immediately following each session.

When the experimental session involved reinforcement, the run lasted until the indicated number of pellets had been delivered. Operant-level and extinction sessions were uniformly 10 minutes in duration. Tray training was accomplished by maintaining pellet delivery every 15 seconds for a total of 50 pellets. Animals failing to eat more than 10 per cent of the pellets were discarded. Tray training always took place at the session immediately preceding the initial conditioning session.

A "self-shaping" procedure was followed for conditioning. The animal was introduced into the cage after a single pellet had been placed in the pellet tray and the lever had been baited with a small amount of food powder. Subsequently, pellet delivery was exclusively contingent upon the occurrence of a criterion response. Animals failing to condition in an hour and a half under this procedure were discarded, but failure happened very infrequently. All subsequent runs were begun with one pellet in the food tray. When intermittent reinforcement schedules were involved, the first criterion response was always reinforced.

Chapter Three

The Differentiation of Response Force, Duration, and Time Integral of Force

A PRELIMINARY ACCOUNT of the sequential emission of response force in the bar-pressing situation appeared some time ago (Notterman, 1959). That report described the data resulting from exposure of a group of six Wistar rats to the usual stages of the learning process, operant level, regular reinforcement, and extinction. The operant-level phase consisted of two 35-minute sessions, followed by 20 minutes of tray-approach training; conditioning was accomplished in four sessions of regular reinforcement, one standard 45-mg. pellet per response, each session terminating upon procurement of approximately 50 pellets; and extinction was limited to two 35-minute sessions. Customary 23-hour deprivation schedules were maintained.

Figure 3-1, which is reproduced from the earlier article, is a response-by-response sequential plot of peak force attained by one of the subjects during the course of the entire experiment. Threshold and criterion (see Chapter 2) were both set at 3.0-gm. peak force.

The data depicted for this subject were characteristic of the remaining five subjects. Noteworthy is the decline in response magnitude over the regular reinforcement sessions; this attenuation is accompanied by a decrease in force variability. Extinction reveals quite the opposite trend: both force magnitude and variability show a sharp increase, and this continues well into extinction.

Figure 3-2 reproduces the customary cumulative-response record obtained during bar-pressing experiments and is for the same animal represented in Fig. 3-1. (The operant-level, conditioning-session 1, and extinction-session 2 data were omitted in the interests of presenting as large a scale as possible.) The broken line represents the slope of conditioning-session 4 and indicates that this, the last session of reg-

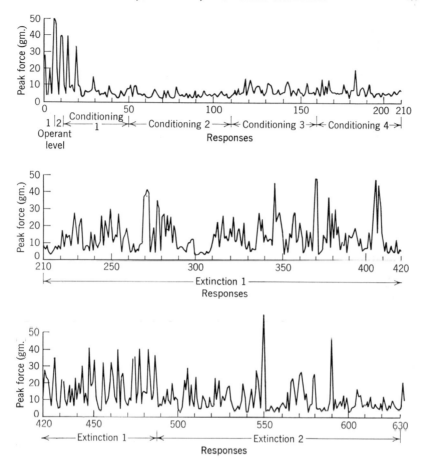

Figure 3-1 Peak force of successive responses for a single subject during operant level, conditioning, and extinction. (After Notterman, 1959.)

ular reinforcement, produced the highest rate during acquisition. As is typical, the beginning of extinction reveals a momentary increase in rate, followed by a general decline.

In comments on the progressive increase in rate over the four regular reinforcement sessions, it was noted:

The rate measure . . . is based upon approximately 50 responses produced by . . . S during each of the regular reinforcement sessions. Accordingly, the increase in rate is *not* the result of a greater number of responses having been emitted during successive, constant total time sessions, but rather

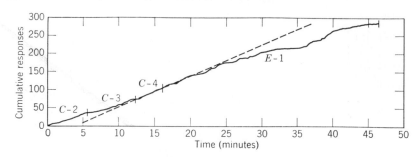

Figure 3-2 Cumulative-response record for subject represented in Fig. 3-1 for the second, third, and fourth days of conditioning, and the first day of extinction. The dashed line indicates the slope of the curve during the last day of conditioning. (After Notterman, 1959.)

the result of the same number of responses having been emitted during progressively shorter sessions. Such being the case, it is clear that it is the dropping out of intervening behavior (i.e., behavior between successive bar presses) which is responsible for the observed rate increases. Considered in this sense, bar-pressing rate is a measure of bar-pressing response strength *relative* to the strength of other ongoing behavior (Notterman, 1959, p. 346).

The reader will recognize this as the sense of the quotation from Skinner (1938) cited in Chapter 1. The article just cited had limited objectives; its purposes were principally (1) to assert that, contrary to earlier accounts (for instance, Keller and Schoenfeld, 1950, p. 50), peak force of response does vary systematically with reinforcement operations, and (2) to suggest that frequency and intensity measures describe different behavioral properties and therefore should not be expected to be positively correlated, of necessity.

The work presented in this chapter seeks to pursue further the analysis within the dimension of force and to extend the inquiry to include response duration and time integral of force. In designing an experiment to meet these objectives, we made the parameter of major interest the quantity that we have defined as "criterion"—the particular value of the selected response dimension that is established by the experimenter as being "reinforcement-procuring." In the experiment described in this chapter, four such criteria were initially specified, and separate groups of subjects were permitted to obtain reinforcement only upon successfully meeting the assigned criterion. The groups and their related criteria are designated: Group I, 2.5-gm. peak force; Group II, 0.8-second duration; Group III, 8.0-gm. peak force; and Group IV, 4.0-gram-second time integral of force.

Several preliminary comments concerning these criteria are in order: (1) regardless of the criterion, the threshold (minimal peak force that defines a response) was kept at 2.5-gm. peak force; (2) for the various devices to register and record a response, it was necessary for the emitted force to have a minimal duration of somewhat less than 1 millisecond; (3) consequently, for Group I any force that qualified as a response, also qualified for reinforcement. This was equivalent to the ordinary bar-pressing situation, but one in which a very light spring is used in the microswitch. It was also the same threshold-criterion relationship that prevailed during the research cited earlier (Notterman, 1959). For Group III a force criterion was again designated, but, unlike the requirement for Group I, the criterion was considerably higher than the threshold. This was similar to the bar-pressing situation in which a typical spring is used so that not all forces exerted upon the bar are sufficient to close the microswitch contacts. It differed from the usual Skinnerian definition of response (maintaining criterion equal to threshold) in that a given force emission of insufficient magnitude to reach criterion was nonetheless recorded as a response if it was at least of 2.5-gm. magnitude. It should also be remembered here that in our procedure the animals were not provided with any exteroceptive stimulus correlate during response emission for the achievement of either threshold or criterion. The microswitch "click" in the conventional Skinnerian apparatus provides such a stimulus correlate.

For Groups II and IV, reinforcement was procured only when a response (2.5-gm. or higher) met the respective criteria of duration or time integral of force. Here too, all responses were recorded, regardless of whether criterion was achieved.

Method

Six animals were randomly assigned to each of the four groups after all 24 subjects had been through a 23-hour deprivation schedule (see Chapter 2). Criterion responses were reinforced with standard 45-mg. pellets. Table 3-1 gives the phases of the experiment, the experimental operations pertaining to each phase, and the group designations in terms of criteria (note that the criteria shift upward in Phase 5).

TABLE 3-1

Experimental Phases and Conditions by Groups, with Reinforcement Criterion Indicated for Each Phase

		Groups			
Phase	Operation	I	II	III	IV
1	Tray-approach training 1 session 40 pellets	none	none	none	none
2	Regular reinforcement (CRF) 20 sessions 35 pellets/session	2.5 gm. (threshold)	0.8 sec.	8 gm.	4 gm.-sec.
3	Extinction I * 3 sessions 10 min./session	2.5 gm. (threshold)	0.8 sec.	8 gm.	4 gm.-sec.
4	Reconditioning 7 sessions 35 pellets/session	2.5 gm. (threshold)	0.8 sec.	8 gm.	4 gm.-sec.
5	Shift (CRF) 14 sessions 35 pellets/session	16 gm.	1.6 sec.	16 gm.	8 gm.-sec.
6	Extinction II * 3 sessions 10 min./session	16 gm.	1.6 sec.	16 gm.	8 gm.-sec.

* Although reinforcement did not occur, a distinction between criterion and noncriterion responses was maintained for data-collection and analysis purposes.

Results and Discussion

Figure 3-3 gives the session-by-session means for Group I for the three characteristics of response recorded (peak force, duration, and time integral of force). The session-by-session mean standard deviation of the criterion (peak force, in this case) is also shown.[1]

[1] For purposes of facilitating comparison, the scales of the separate response dimensions in each of these graphs have been kept constant from group to group (Figs. 3-3, -7, -11, and -15). Also, the data for the mean of the criterion dimension, as well as for the standard deviation of that dimension, appear in solid circles throughout.

The peak-force data show a gradual drift during regular or continuous reinforcement (CRF) from approximately 16 gm. to approximately 7 gm. as a function of sessions. (The broken lines indicate the value of the reinforcement criteria.) The extinction and reconditioning results are what might be expected, on the basis of prior findings. When the criterion is shifted from 2.5 to 16 gm. (Phase 5), the response level also shifts and in the appropriate direction. Extinction following the shift generates forces higher than those prevailing during earlier extinction (after CRF at 2.5 gm.).

These findings concerning the effect of reinforcement operations upon the level of force emission (Fig. 3-3-A) and the variability (Fig. 3-3-D) are consistent with the earlier work cited in the beginning of the chapter. Information not heretofore available, however, is provided by the duration and time-integral-of-force graphs.

Examination of parts B and C of Fig. 3-3 reveals a striking phenomenon. Even though the organisms are not being deliberately and selectively reinforced for particular values of duration or time integral of force, the effect of reinforcing for the peak-force criterion appears also to influence these noncriterion dimensions of response. This observation immediately poses the serious question of whether the experimenter's presumably selective reinforcement operations are uniquely or even principally affecting the particular response dimension reinforced. On the basis of pilot work, this problem had been anticipated and, in fact, is largely responsible for the "shift" feature in the present design (Phase 5). This was the reasoning. If changes in response force and duration were indeed correlated, then (hopefully) this correlation would decrease as a function of increased exposure of any particular response dimension to selective reinforcement. Eventually, a point would be reached where, if the criterion were shifted to some new value, the dimension being reinforced would show a tendency to conform to the shift, while the other dimensions would not. Returning to Fig. 3-3, one sees from part A that the peak force of response shifts upward in accordance with the elevation in criterion (from 2.5 to 16 gm.). But one also sees that the duration of response (part B) likewise increases as a consequence of the change in force criterion. Accordingly, two conclusions are suggested. First, in partial answer to the question that has been raised, the effects of selective reinforcement do not appear to be unique to the dimension being "shaped." Second, the design strategy failed to produce uniqueness by the shift procedure. From this discussion, it is apparent that the task of demonstrating that a particular response dimension is principally (if not

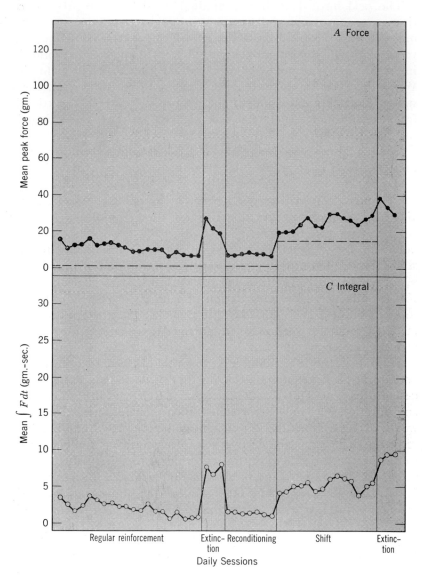

Figure 3-3 Mean peak force (*A*), mean duration (*B*), mean time integral of force (*C*), and standard deviations of the peak-force distributions (*D*) as a function of successive days for *Group I*. The criterion is shown by the dashed lines in (*A*) for the reinforced phases of the study.

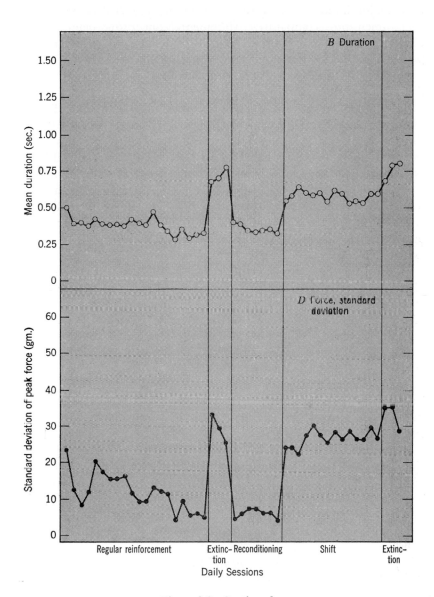

Figure 3-3 Continued.

uniquely) influenced by the present selective reinforcement operations is of major importance. Moreover, since we are dealing with disparate dimensions, comparative statements concerning magnitudes of observed differences cannot be readily made. We shall return to this problem in the section titled "Intergroup Comparisons."

Figures 3-4 through 3-6 show for Group I the relative frequency distributions of the indicated response dimensions on the first day of extinction and on the last days of reconditioning and shift. The median in each of these curves is identified by the open circle. Although the difference in scale of step intervals, as well as the dimensions themselves, makes direct interdimension comparison impossible, the distribution figures are of value in indicating the specific effects of selective reinforcement within each response property. Of particular interest here are the distributions for the last day of reconditioning and of shift, for these presumably reflect the best performance of the organisms on each of the two criterion values to which the group was exposed. Note, for example, the extensive difference in the median peak force for these two days. A change in the same direction can be observed for the duration of these responses; but again, the reader must be cautioned against comparing the actual differences, because of the unlike dimensions and scale intervals. The same observation applies, of course, to the time integral of force distributions. Comparable with the group mean as a function of sessions data (Fig. 3-3) is evidence of the effects on the peak force dimension of selective reinforcement of peak force; but the other dimensions are also influenced in the same direction, and because of the "apples–versus–pears" nature of the comparison, a hierarchical or comparative statement of effects cannot casually be made.

Regarding the data of Group II, it will be recalled that the criterion was 0.8 second. Each response (defined as 2.5-gm. peak force or higher) had to persist for 0.8 second or longer to earn reinforcement. The reader is reminded that in this experiment no exteroceptive stimulus was available to the subject indicative of criterion achievement, and that reinforcement, when earned, would not occur until the response was terminated.

Figure 3-7 gives the group means by sessions for the three dimensions of response investigated and the group mean standard deviation for the criterion dimension. Examining part *B* first, one sees that the acquisition curve of the criterion dimension (duration) is an increasing, negatively accelerated function of training; accordingly, its form is quite different from the curve characteristic of the criterion dimen-

sion for Group I, which is a *decreasing,* negatively accelerated function. That the value of the dimension, rather than the quality of the
dimension itself, determines whether the acquisition curve is an increasing or decreasing function is suggested by examination of the
shift data for peak force in Fig. 3-3. Note that this curve is an increasing function. Apparently, if the value of the criterion dimension
is higher than either operant or prevalent levels, the organism will
adjust the level of response dimension until (within the limits to be
suggested subsequently) sufficient numbers of responses are reinforced
to sustain behavior.

Despite the form of the function shown in Fig. 3-7-*B,* the standard
deviation data for this dimension result in a declining function. The
possibility immediately presents itself that, within any criterion dimension or value, a consistently useful measure of learning and performance is afforded by examination of the standard deviation: the
lower the standard deviation, the better the learning or performance.
Although the general phenomenon of decreasing variability with
learning is by no means a new finding, the possible extension of this
phenomenon to the various dimensions of response perhaps increases
the usefulness of the observation.

Part *A* of this figure is remarkable in its depiction of extremely
high values of emitted peak force. These magnitudes, typically in the
range of 40 to 60 gm., are reached even though the organism need
generate only 2.5 gm. per response. Why is the organism so "inef-
ficient"? Although several possibilities exist, the line of inquiry that
seems to us to hold most promise for future investigation is this. It
has already been suggested that force and duration are correlated, and,
in fact, Figs. 3-7-*A* and -*B* augment the observation that force and
duration tend to rise and fall together. What needs to be accounted
for is the *magnitude* of the force emission in the duration group. We
will advance the argument now that duration per se is physically nonexistent for the organism. When called upon to respond to a duration criterion, the animal tends to fill the elapsing time with cues of
response-induced origin. We believe that the source of these feedback
cues lies principally in cutaneous and kinesthetic return from the bar-
pressing response. In short, the Group II animals press the bar harder
and harder, until the length of time they take to reach the level of
response indicated in Fig. 3-7-*A* produces the duration shown in part
B.

We are aware that this hypothesis poses a riddle within a riddle.
Why, after all, should the animals press harder in the first place?

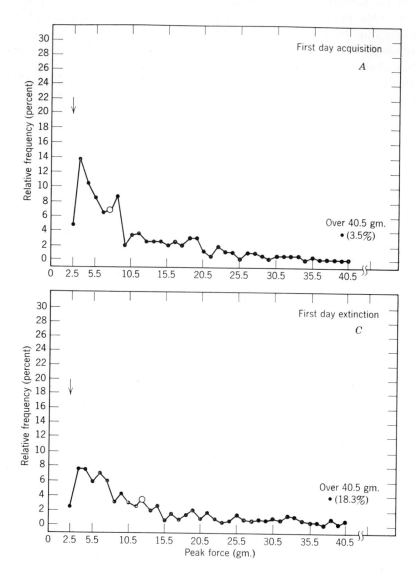

Figure 3-4 Relative frequency distributions of *peak force* of response for Group I on the first (*A*) and last (*B*) days of acquisition, the first day of extinction (*C*), and the last days of both reconditioning and criterion shift (*D*). For each curve the criterion is indicated by an arrow, the median by a circle.

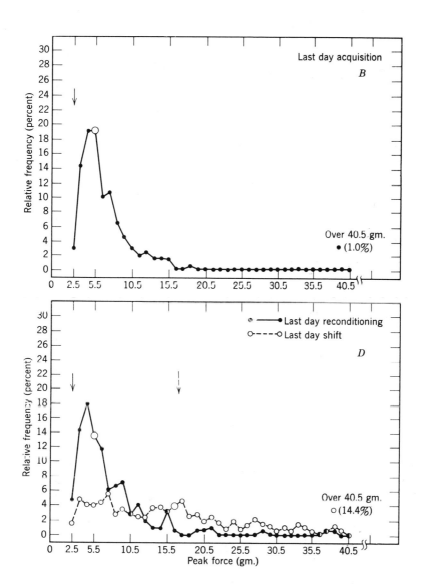

Figure 3-4   Continued.

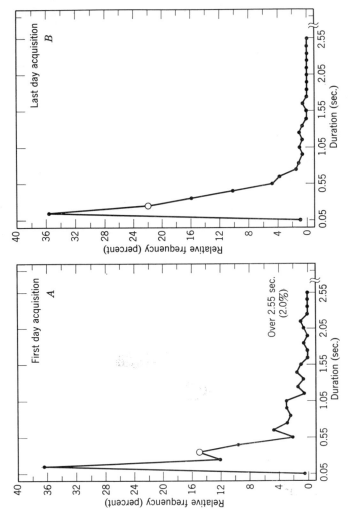

Figure 3-5 Relative frequency distributions of response *duration* for Group I on the first (*A*) and last (*B*) days of acquisition, the first day of extinction (*C*), and the last days of both reconditioning and and criterion shift (*D*). The medians of the distributions are indicated by a circle.

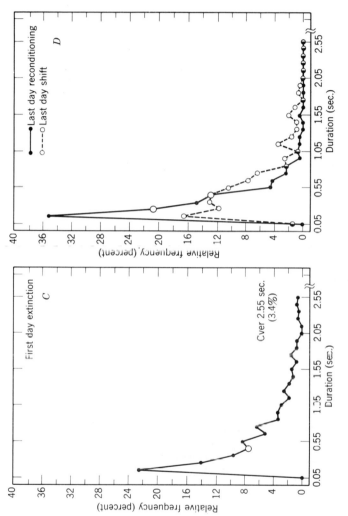

Figure 3-5   Continued.

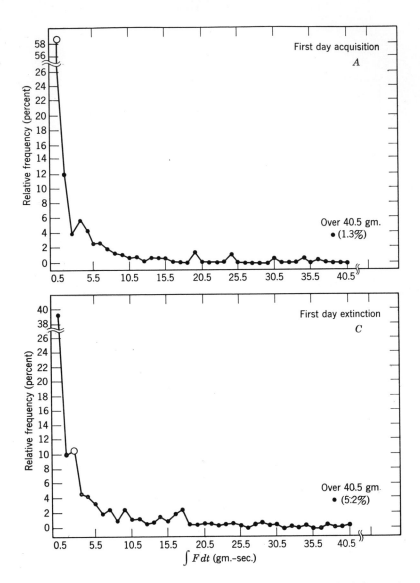

Figure 3-6 Relative frequency distributions of the *time integral* of force of response for Group I on the first (*A*) and last (*B*) days of acquisition, the first day
of extinction (*C*), and the last days of both reconditioning and criterion shift (*D*).
The medians of the distributions are indicated by a circle.

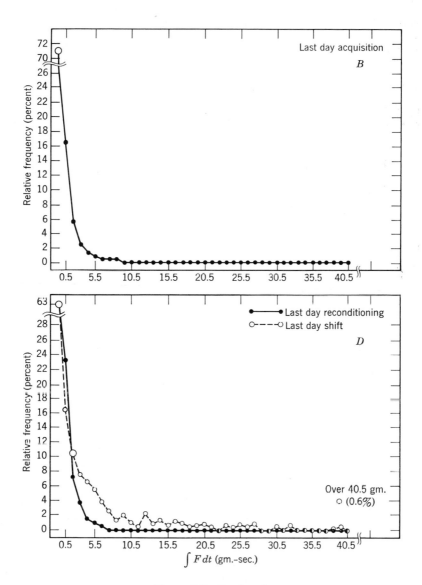

Figure 3-6 Continued.

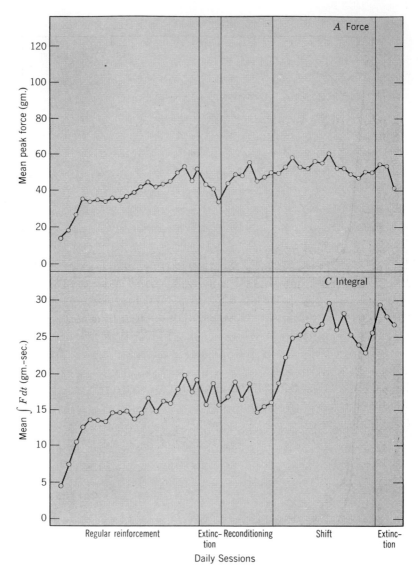

Figure 3-7 Mean peak force (*A*), mean duration (*B*), mean time integral of force (*C*), and standard deviations of the response-duration distributions (*D*) as a function of successive days for *Group II*. The criterion is shown by the dashed lines in (*B*) for the reinforced phases of the study.

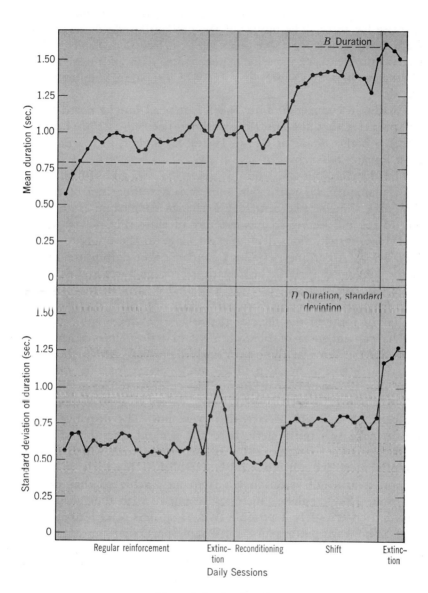

Figure 3-7   Continued.

Is this related to the rise in force, during extinction, of Group I? If so, why do not the extinction data of Group II show a similar increase for force? The nature of the extinction effect upon response force is of such importance for various fields in psychology that its general problems, and specific experimental data addressed to several alternative hypotheses, are the subject of a separate chapter (Chapter 5).

Finally, in connection with Fig. 3-7, it need but be noted for present purposes that the effort dimension (specified as time integral of force) is higher than for Group I; indeed, higher, as it will be seen, than for any other group.

The distributions of Group II (Figs. 3-8, -9, and -10) are largely self-explanatory. Of particular interest is a comparison of the duration data showing the anticipated change in median from the last day of reconditioning to the last day of shift (Fig. 3-9-D) with the peak force distributions depicting a change in the opposite direction (Fig. 3-8-D). Accordingly, we may conclude that despite the existence of the previously remarked correlation between force and duration, a change in one need not produce a related change in the other.

In general, the data of Group III (Figs. 3-11, -12, -13, and -14) are similar in form to the data of the other peak-force subjects, Group I. The consequences of reinforcement and nonreinforcement operations are the same as those previously described. Although a higher criterion (8 gm. as opposed to 2.5 gm.) was set for this group, it is clear that the combined means for the subjects reflect attainment of this criterion (Fig. 3-11-A). This is not to say that *all* responses were "successful"; in point of fact, they were not. The distribution data, which make this quite clear, raise the general question of whether the subjects vary systematically in the degree with which they consistently meet the various criteria established for each of the four groups. Is an 8-gm. criterion less frequently achieved than a 2.5-gm. criterion? How do these "successes" compare with the "success" of a duration criterion? Is it possible that, regardless of criterion, subjects tend to improve performance until some particular percentage of responses is reinforced and then stabilize at that level? Cast in more specific terminology, do organisms tend to establish themselves on a variable ratio schedule even though it may be possible, with some additional effort or pressure, to establish themselves on a 100 per cent reinforcement schedule? If so, is this self-imposed variable ratio consistent from criterion to criterion? What role does proprioceptive discrimination (as opposed to an effort factor) play in this? A preliminary attempt to deal with some of these questions is made in the Intergroup Comparison Section.

Figure 3-11-*B* permits us to observe that mean duration of response is approximately twice as high for Group III during acquisition as for Group I. This finding is consistent with previous speculation concerning the role played by duration as a response dimension (see page 29).

Since both mean peak force and mean duration were higher for Group III than for Group I, it comes as no surprise to note that time integral of force (Fig. 3-11-*C*), which is partially dependent upon each of these parameters, is likewise higher. The variability data (Fig. 3-11-*D*) show the expected drift downward, with increased training, and the reversal of this trend during the extinction and shift phases. The shift, it should be noted, at least initially produces a sharp decrease in the relative frequency of reinforcement.

In comparing the peak force distributions of Group III (Figs. 3-12-*A*, -*B*, -*C*, and -*D*) with those of Group I (Figs. 3-4-*A*, -*B*, -*C*, -*D*) we see that except for the shift data, Group III shows less of a modal tendency than Group I. (The shift condition was identical for both groups, with the criterion set at 16 gm.) Since Group I was operating on a 2.5-gm. criterion, and Group III on an 8-gm. criterion, it is possible that the difference in form of distribution during acquisition and reconditioning can be attributed to differences in either the discriminative capacity or response effort required at these disparate criteria levels. However, neither of these alternatives taken singly seems to us to be quite sufficient. An 8-gm. requirement is not a very demanding one; the animals are capable of exerting forces up to several times this magnitude (recall, for example, the 40-to-60-gm. range of the duration-criterion animals, Group II). Yet, some 35 per cent of the responses made by Group III during the last days of acquisition are below criterion. Similarly, the relative rapidity with which the various criteria come to shape behavior, together with the phenomena of "band discrimination" (to be discussed in Chapters 5 and 6), suggest that the discriminative capacity of the subjects is better than would appear from cursory examination of the distributions. At least for the present, it would seem that the most reasonable account of the decreased modality of Group III distributions rests on the combined circumstances of discriminative capacity, emitted effort, and the role of reinforcement in maintaining behavior. In short, the suggestion is strong that the animals "maximize" by generating response levels that are qualitatively and quantitatively consistent with the

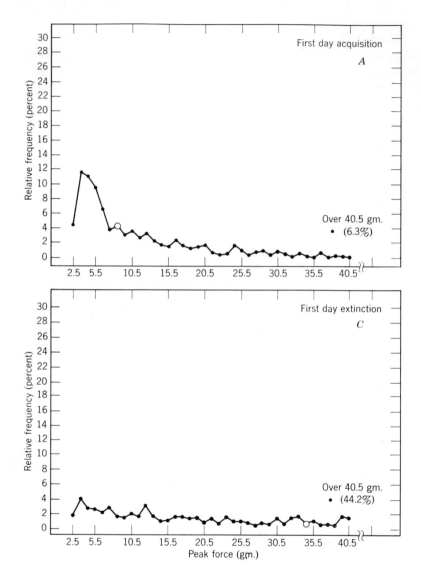

Figure 3-8 Relative frequency distributions of *peak force* of response for Group II on the first (*A*) and last (*B*) days of acquisition, the first day of extinction (*C*), and the last days of both reconditioning and criterion shift (*D*). The medians of the distributions are indicated by a circle.

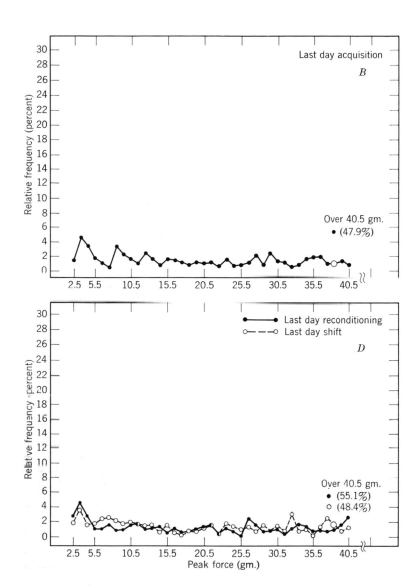

Figure 3-8   Continued.

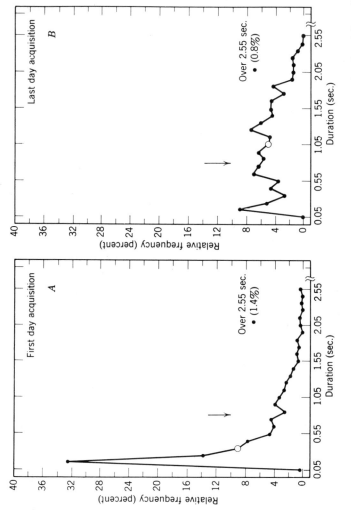

Figure 3-9 Relative frequency distributions of response *durations* for Group II on the first (*A*) and last (*B*) days of acquisition, the first day of extinction (*C*), and the last days of both reconditioning and criterion shift (*D*). For each curve the criterion is indicated by an arrow, the median by a circle.

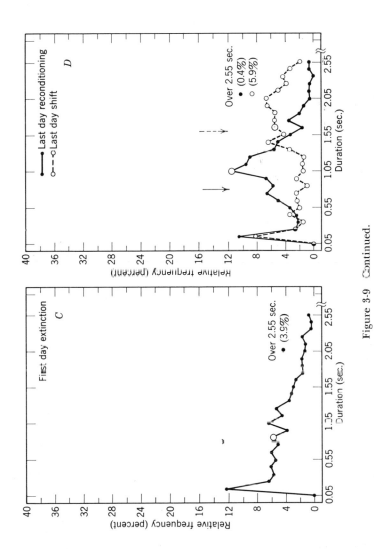

Figure 3-9 Continued.

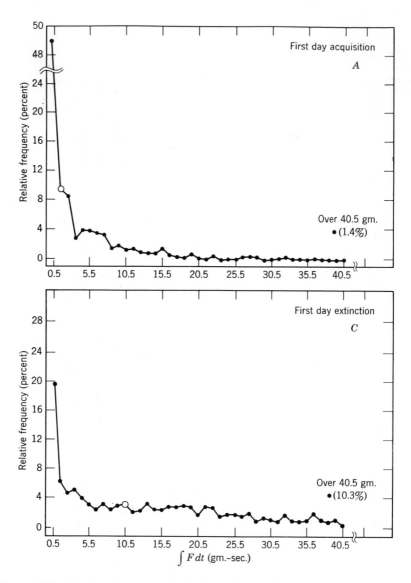

Figure 3-10 Relative frequency distributions of the *time integral* of force of response for Group II on the first (*A*) and last (*B*) days of acquisition, the first day of extinction (*C*), and the last days of both reconditioning and criterion shift (*D*). The medians of the distribution are indicated by a circle.

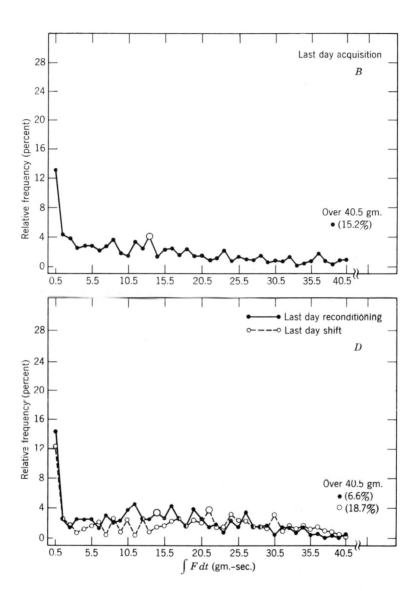

Figure 3-10   Continued.

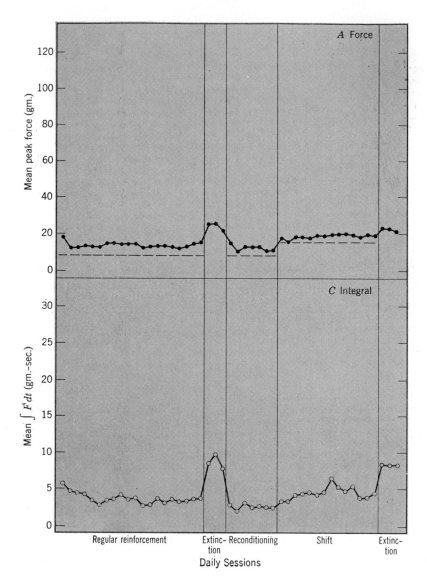

Figure 3-11 Mean peak force (*A*), mean duration (*B*), mean time integral of force (*C*), and standard deviations of the peak force distributions (*D*) as a function of successive days for *Group III*. The criterion is shown by the dashed lines in (*A*) for the reinforced phases of the study.

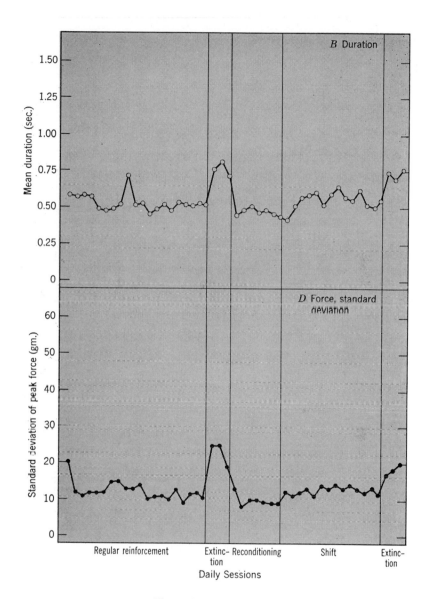

Figure 3-11   Continued.

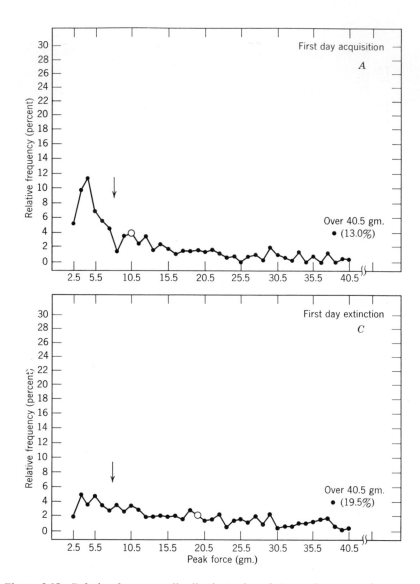

Figure 3-12 Relative frequency distributions of *peak force* of response for Group III on the first (*A*) and last (*B*) days of acquisition, the first day of extinction (*C*), and the last days of both reconditioning and criterion shift (*D*). For each curve the criterion is indicated by an arrow, the median by a circle.

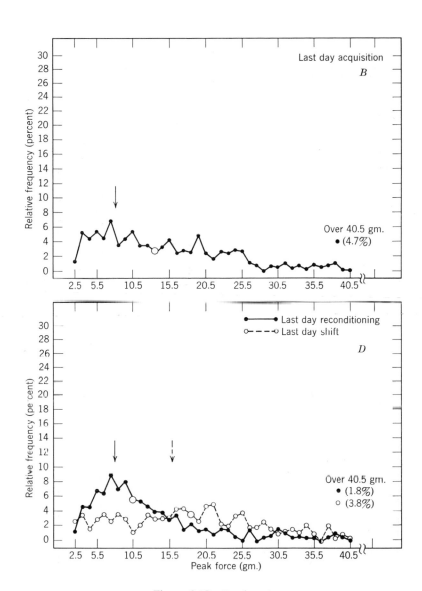

Figure 3-12   Continued.

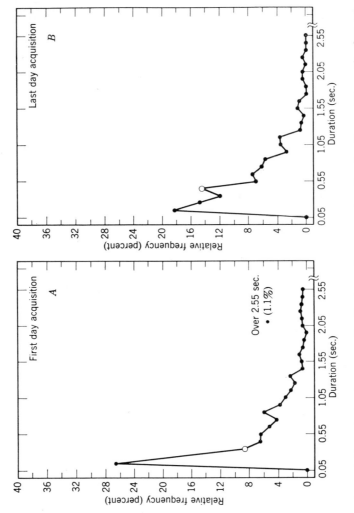

Figure 3-13 Relative frequency distributions of response *duration* for Group III on the first (*A*) and last (*B*) days of acquisition, the first day of extinction (*C*), and the last days of both reconditioning and criterion shift (*D*). The medians of the distributions are indicated by a circle.

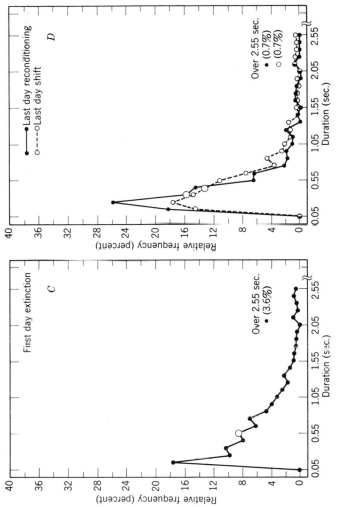

Figure 3-13 Continued.

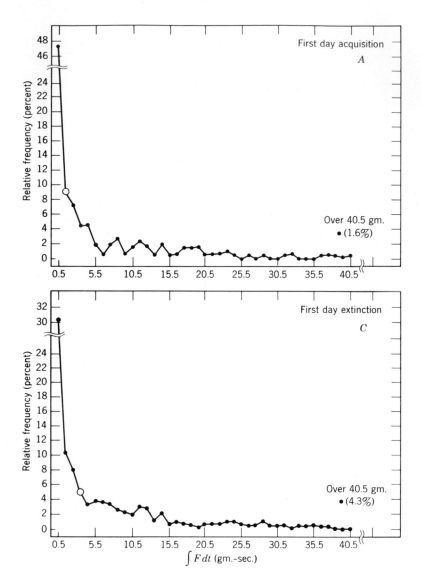

Figure 3-14 Relative frequency distributions of the *time integral* of force of response for Group III on the first (*A*) and last (*B*) days of acquisition, the first day of extinction (*C*), and the last days of both reconditioning and criterion shift (*D*). The medians of the distributions are indicated by a circle.

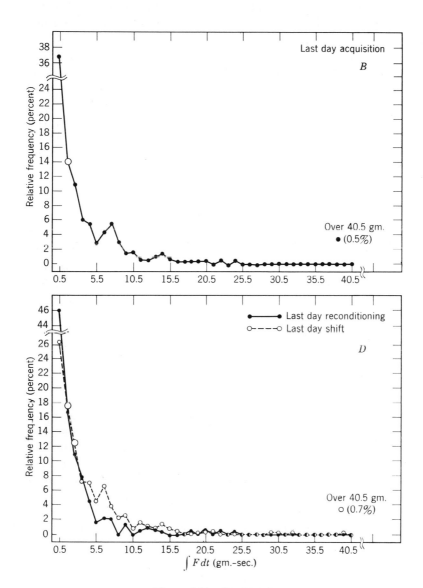

Figure 3-14 Continued.

criterion (or reinforcement contingencies), but that something less than 100 per cent reinforcement is sufficient to maintain this behavior.

The data relative to Group IV (time-integral-of-force criterion) are shown in Figs. 3-15, -16, -17, and -18. The unique feature of this group was its ability to obtain reinforcement by means of any combination of force and duration, provided the area under the response curve (instantaneous force as a function of time) exceeded a lower limit of 4 gram-seconds during acquisition and 8 gram-seconds during shift. Examination of the group mean time-integral-of-force curves (Fig. 3-15-C), as well as the standard deviation of these means (Fig. 3-15-D) reveals characteristics quite similar to those obtained for Groups I and III. Particularly convincing is the finding that the standard deviation decreases during acquisition and reconditioning and increases during extinction.

Do the animals actually come under the influence of an effort criterion, independently of force and duration? Figures 3-15-A and -B indicate that both of these dimensions reveal an upward slope during acquisition and during shift. Notable is the observation that duration seems to carry the brunt of behavioral change during extinction, reflecting, perhaps, the high level of peak force present immediately prior to extinction. The relative increase in any of the dimensions during extinction appears dependent on the level previously maintained with reinforcement. In any event, it appears that both force and duration of response are sensitive to an effort criterion set by the experimenter. But is one used more than the other? The angles of the slopes (A versus B) during acquisition are of no help in determining the answer to this question, because of the differences in scale and in dimension. When shift occurs, is the effect upon time integral of force greater than it is for either peak force alone or duration alone? Again, the differences in scale and in dimension can be misleading. The importance of this question is such, however, that it is re-examined in the next section, where a procedure for determining the answer is described. Since the described procedure is related to comparisons of distributions, comment on Figs. 3-16, -17, and -18 is withheld for the time being.

Intergroup Comparisons

There are several intergroup comparisons that are of a sufficiently general nature to warrant special comment. In addition, we attempt in this section to deal with the unresolved issues raised earlier in this chapter.

Rate of Response

There are two features of Fig. 3-19 that immediately strike the eye. The first is the observation that, regardless of criterion, all groups reach approximately the same level of response frequency by the end of acquisition. The second is that the curves show a more gradual ascent than is typical for the usual bar-pressing data. In connection with the gradual ascent, we have examined sufficient numbers of individual records to assure ourselves that this is not an averaging phenomenon. Rather, we attribute the slower rise to the physical characteristics of the manipulandum, both as to smaller contact area than usual and the essentially zero amplitude of excursion. Additionally, the absence of the usual microswitch click probably produces some delay in the animal's learning to discriminate "response" from other behaviors.

The apparent stabilization of the animals at the same rate, despite differences in criterion, is surprising. The curves under examination show all responses (any force emission of 2.5 gm. or higher) and not exclusively reinforced or criterion responses. Since the figures indicate all responses, reinforced or not, and since the rate of response reaches the same level, the question of the relationship between numbers of unreinforced and reinforced responses becomes important. Do the subjects establish themselves on a self-imposed variable ratio schedule that, within limits, is independent of criterion? For the moment, suffice it to observe that despite the wide variation in peak force, duration, and time integral of force revealed earlier in this chapter, *the rate-of-response data give no indication of the systematic group diversity of these measures.* Surely, it is excessive to attribute to coincidence the attainment of the same rates under criterion conditions so varied, especially when these rates contain both unreinforced and reinforced components. We will comment further on this issue in connection with Fig. 3-23.

Strip-Chart Recordings

With the aid of a strip-chart recorder, it is possible to examine the instantaneous emission of force as a function of time. For the present work, this examination is regrettably limited to mere visual inspec-

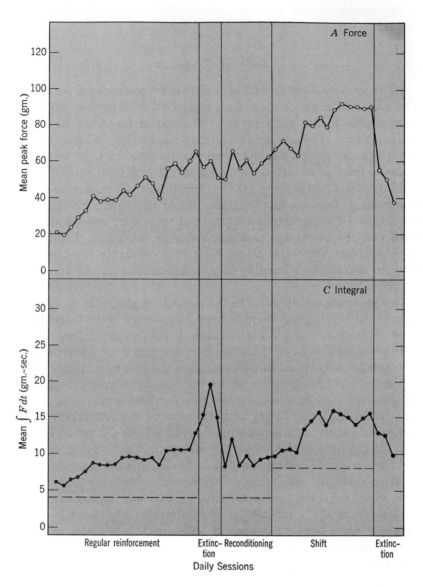

Figure 3-15   Mean peak force (*A*), mean duration (*B*), mean time integral of force (*C*), and standard deviations of the time integral of force distributions (*D*) as a function of successive days for *Group IV*. The criterion is shown by the dashed lines in (*C*) for the reinforced phases of the study.

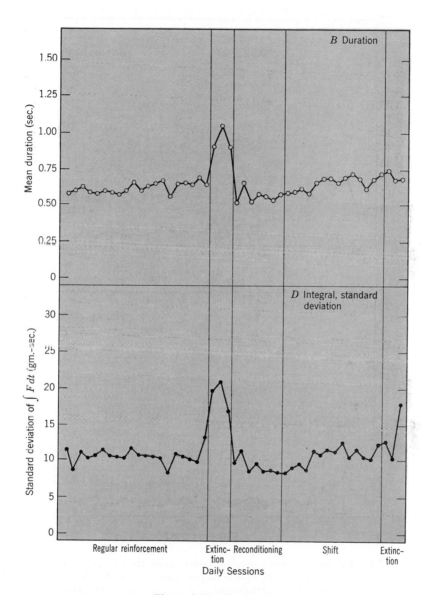

Figure 3-15   Continued.

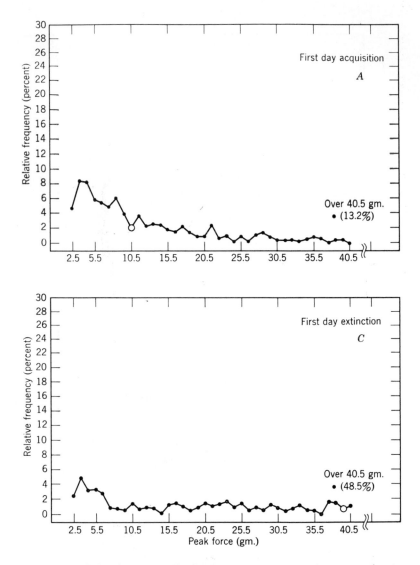

Figure 3-16   Relative frequency distributions of *peak force* of response for Group IV on the first (*A*) and last (*B*) days of acquisition, the first day of extinction (*C*), and the last days of both reconditioning and criterion shift (*D*). The medians of the distributions are indicated by a circle.

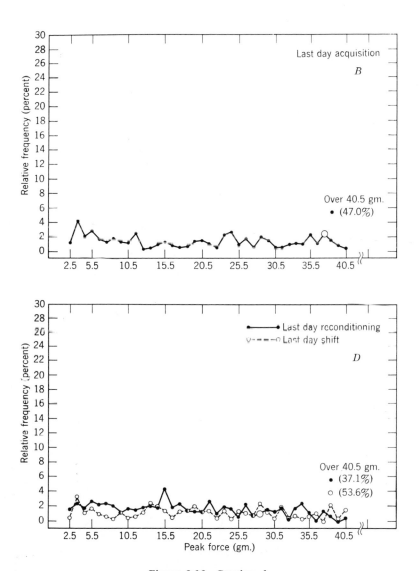

Figure 3-16 Continued.

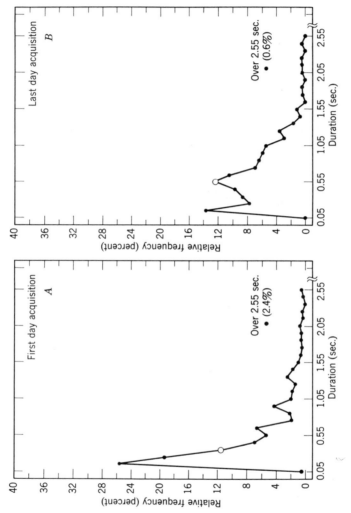

Figure 3-17 Relative frequency distributions of response *duration* for Group IV on the first (*A*) and last (*B*) days of acquisition, the first day of extinction (*C*), and the last days of both reconditioning and criterion shift (*D*). The medians of the distributions are indicated by a circle.

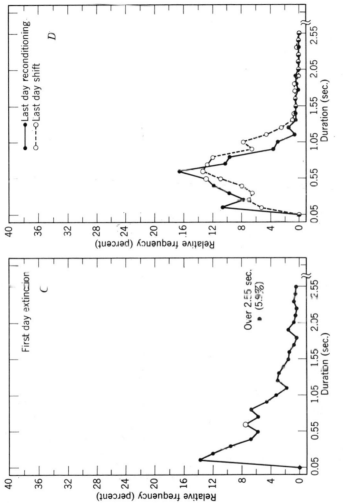

Figure 3-17 Continued.

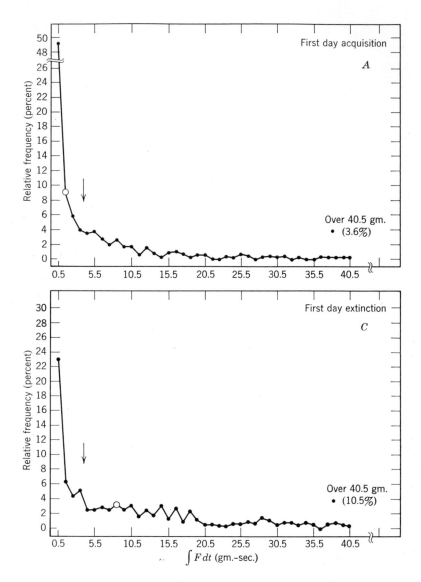

Figure 3-18 Relative frequency distributions of the *time integral* of force of response for Group IV on the first (*A*) and last (*B*) days of acquisition, the first day of extinction (*C*), and the last days of both reconditioning and criterion shift (*D*). For each curve the reinforcement criterion is indicated by an arrow, the median by a circle.

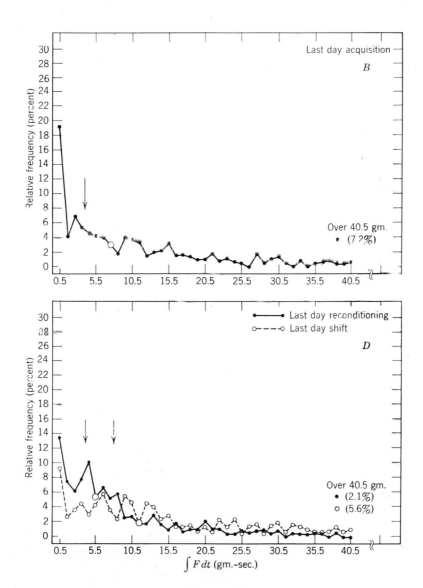

Figure 3-18 Continued.

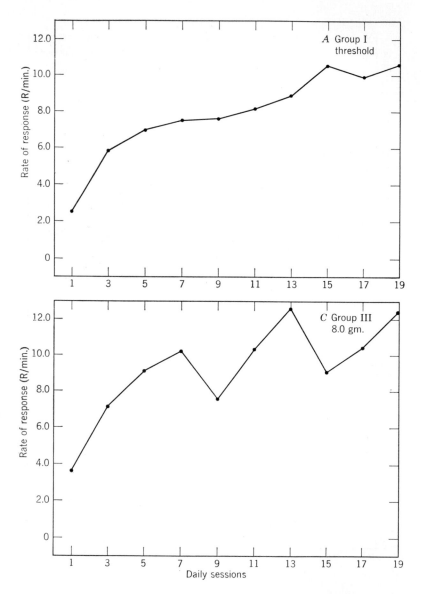

Figure 3-19 Rate of response as a function of successive days during acquisition for each of the four groups.

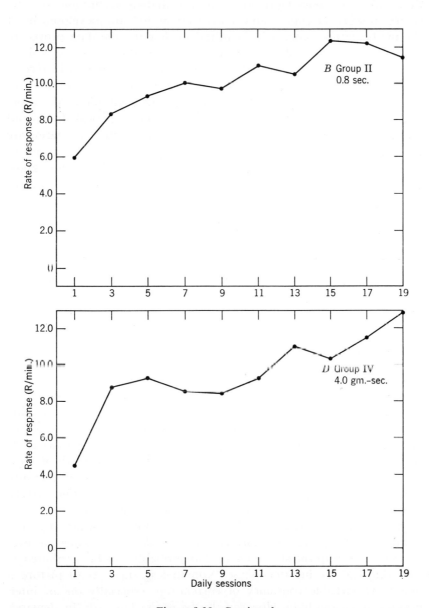

Figure 3-19 Continued.

tion. Although some more sophisticated analytic techniques (for instance, power-spectrum analysis) were attempted, the development of the mathematical procedures required to describe the data proved to be beyond the scope of this volume. However, the points we wish to make are adequately revealed by visual examination of the recordings. For example, if we compare Fig. 3-20-*A* with parts *B* and *C* of the figure, we see immediately that *B* contains a sample of duration-criterion response, that *C* contains a sample of high peak force, and that *A* contains a sample of low-peak force. Of particular interest are the "perturbations" observed in *B:* these high-frequency variations in peak force are typical of the duration animals. We do not know whether the variations are merely "tremor" or whether they represent a form of kinesthetic "scanning" that provides the sensory analog of duration discrimination based on force feedback.

No sample of an effort-criterion animal is provided because, as noted in the earlier discussion of Group IV, the subjects modified both force and duration. A typical mode of responding was less apparent for the animals in this group than for the animals in the three groups represented in Fig. 3-20.

Correlation between Force and Duration

On an intuitive basis, it seems quite reasonable to expect a correlation between force and duration of response. Other things being equal, it should take more time to reach a higher force than a lower one. Two aspects of this assumed correlation cannot, however, be readily described in the absence of empirical data: first, the extent of the correlation; and second, whether the correlation varies systematically with the criterion. Figure 3-21 provides information on both of these points. The mean correlations for the subjects in each of the groups are remarkably similar, varying about the value of .60. The correlations were computed on a response-by-response basis, individually for each animal. The intergroup differences are not significant. It is also worth observing that the correlation does decrease somewhat over the course of acquisition, an effect that probably can be attributed to the "shaping" during that phase. Nonetheless, the over-all picture is one of remarkable constancy of correlation, especially on an intergroup comparison basis. How can this be reconciled with the demands of the different criteria? If the animals come to respond in accordance with the criteria of the respective groups, should this not result in serious attenuation of the correlation? What happens is simply that

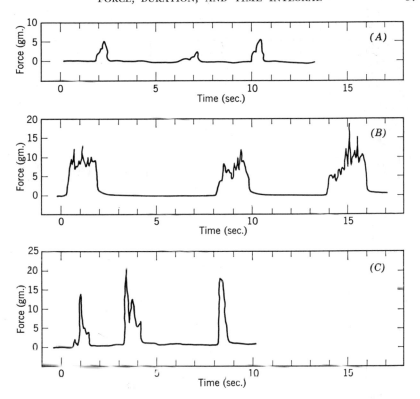

Figure 3-20 Sample force emissions from strip-chart records. The reinforcement criteria are 2.5-gm. peak force (A), 1.6 sec. duration (B), and 16-gm. peak force (C). Coordinates have been added.

the magnitude of either duration or force changes with the specific character of the criterion, but within the range of variation the ordering of duration with force remains fairly constant. Obviously, correlation as a statistic does not reflect actual magnitudes, but only relative position.

Evidence for Differentiation

Since peak force and duration are correlated, they usually, but not inevitably, rise and fall together. As was noted in the descriptions of Figs. 3-3 to 3-6 and Fig. 3-15, the experimenter must defend the assertion that his selective reinforcement operations are indeed more effective with the dimension that is being differentiated than with the other

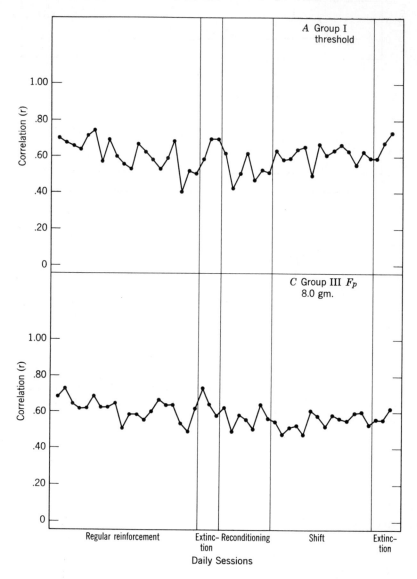

Figure 3-21   Product-moment correlation coefficients of peak force and duration of response as a function of successive days for each of the groups. Correlations are based upon individual responses and averaged across animals within a group.

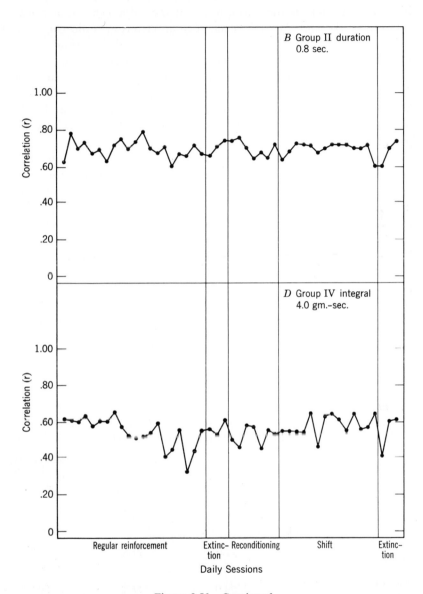

Figure 3-21 Continued.

dimensions of response. Table 3-2 depicts our attempt to cope with this problem. Here is the reasoning that the table reflects, as applied to Groups I, II, and III. Since each shift in criterion (following initial extinction and reconditioning) was in an upward direction (2.5 gm. to 16 gm.; 0.8 second to 1.6 seconds; 8 gm. to 16 gm.), then it should follow that the distribution of the response-criterion dimension would also shift upward. Moreover, we should expect that even if force and duration were correlated, the effect of the shift upon their distributions would be greater for whichever dimension was selectively reinforced.

However, since the units differ, the shift-induced absolute differences in location of the 50th percentile of the reconditioning force and duration distributions, respectively, cannot be validly compared. It *is* valid, on the other hand, to make the following comparisons: for each dimension, a median value (in grams or seconds) exists on the last day of reconditioning (Phase 4); because of the elevation of the criterion during shift (Phase 5) we would expect that this value would—for shift—fall *below* the new 50th percentile (or shift median); moreover, even if both force and duration show this trend, we would expect that that response property that was selectively reinforced would fall lower in its respective shift distribution. Consider the data of Table 3-2 for Group I. This table shows that the median values

TABLE 3-2

Percentile in "Shift" Distribution (Last Day, Phase 5) Attained by Median Value of "Reconditioning" Distribution (Last Day, Phase 4), for the Three Response Properties

	Force (gm.)	Duration (sec.)	Time Integral (gm.-sec.)
Group I (threshold, 2.5 gm.)	14.4	27.5	23.1
Group II (duration)	57.0	21.8	34.3
Group III (force, 8 gm.)	24.9	36.2	30.3
Group IV (time integral)	34.5	35.2	26.8

for peak force, duration, and time integral of force during Phase 4 attain percentiles of 14.4, 27.5, and 23.1, respectively, in the Phase 5 distributions. We can only interpret these data to mean that the upward shift in criterion (in going from Phase 4 to Phase 5) was most effective where we would expect it to be most effective, that is, with peak force, the specific response dimension that provides the criterion. As can be seen from the table, each of the other groups reveals the same effect. The lowest shift percentile for prior (reconditioning) median values lies in the column appropriate to the dimension of the criterion.

Again, limiting the discussion for the moment to the first three groups, and to the force and duration properties only, we may obtain some notion of the reliability of the foregoing observations by examining the behavior of the individual animals. By the null hypothesis, each of the 18 animals (pooled regardless of group) could, upon exposure to Phase 5, have shown a greater shift in either the force dimension or the duration dimension, regardless of the criterion employed. (The prediction, of course, is that all 18 subjects would have shown the greater shift-effect in the dimension appropriate to the criterion.) Thus, a twofold contingency table suggests itself as a suitable test and is shown in Table 3-3. The χ^2 computation is routine and is 10.88, which at one degree of freedom is beyond the 0.01 level of confidence.

The data for Group IV are more difficult to interpret. It is conceivable that time integral of force (or "effort") is shaped independently of either peak force or duration. That is, a single subject may alternatively emit a high peak force of short duration or a low peak force of long duration. On the other hand, the integral may, for different subjects, reduce itself to essentially exclusive use of either

TABLE 3-3

The Effect of Shift upon Criterion and Noncriterion Dimensions of Response (Number of Animals Displaying Shift)

	Criterion	Noncriterion
Expected (null hypothesis)	9	9
Observed	16	2

$$\chi^2 = \sum \frac{(O - E)^2}{E} = 10.88$$

one or the other means of generating the time integral. Table 3-2 shows that, for the group as a whole, peak force and duration are similarly influenced by the change from the reconditioning criterion (4 gram-seconds) to the shift criterion (8 gram-seconds), and that the time integral itself is most effective. But this finding is not statistically reliable. Moreover, in going from the 4-gram-second criterion to 8 gram-seconds, two subjects show greater lability in force than duration, and four subjects show the reverse.

Apart from the apparent lack of any consistent force or duration pattern to which all subjects subscribe, there is a further complication. While an increase in peak force affects the time integral of force in the same way that an increase in duration affects it, there is no evidence that the behavioral consequences of peak-force increase and of duration increase are identical. With peak force, it is reasonable to assume that there is a physiological limit of force exertion that acts to attenuate the occurrence of very high peak forces. With duration, it is equally reasonable to assume that "holding" a response runs into the problems presented by delay of reinforcement operations. Hence, it is probably *not* correct to argue that variation in peak force and variation in duration are equally effective behaviorally in establishing a given value of time integral of force. The separate effects of extended limits of force exertion and of increased duration of response could not be equal, except by coincidence. The argument that there are factors that serve to limit the reciprocal roles of high peak force and long response duration in establishing a given value of time integral of force, leads directly to the prediction that, other things being equal, the subject's responses should be shaped in a manner reflecting such limits. The consequences of these limits should be such as to generate *average* (not peak) forces that should tend to be higher for the group under discussion than for any of the others.[2] Subjects, in other words, should compromise between the Scylla of high peak force and the Charybdis of long response duration, and Fig. 3-22 shows that they do. The absolute difference in $\bar{F}$ between the last day of reconditioning and the last day of shift is greater for this group than for any other. Group I shows a greater relative increase in $\bar{F}$, but it must be remembered that in the shift phase this group underwent a large criterion change (2.5-gm. to 16.0-gm. peak force), not a mere doubling of criterion. The comparison between Group II and Group IV is particularly interesting. Although both groups display approximately

---

2 The average force or $\bar{F}$ is obtained by dividing the $\int F\, dt$ by t.

equal $\bar{F}$ at the end of reconditioning, the shift clearly affects the two groups differently.

All in all, our examination of the Group IV data leads us to the tentative conclusion that the use of time integral of force as a response criterion results in the development of a "sustained-force" response, which manifests itself mathematically as average force.

Criterion Responses and Self-Imposed Variable Ratio Reinforcement

One of the consequences of mensuration operations as applied to the specification of responses is that a clear-cut distinction can be made between an event qualifying as a response ("threshold") and an event qualifying as a reinforced response ("criterion"). This is not to be confused with temporal (fixed-interval) or occurrence (fixed-ratio) schedules in which, to be sure, all responses are likewise not reinforced. The distinction lies in the fact that the occasion for reinforcement in the various conventional schedule situations does not depend upon some intrinsic response property but rather upon the temporal separation between responses or upon the number of responses emitted. In the research reported in this chapter, all animals, regardless of group, were permitted to obtain reinforcement on a CRF basis, provided each response met the respective experimenter-imposed criteria. As is obvious from the various distributions shown in the preceding figures, the subjects were far from being completely "successful" in meeting the requirements for reinforcement.

Figure 3-23 gives the proportion of total responses that fulfilled the criterion requirement on each of the sessions for the indicated phases. Note that points are not shown for the conditioning and reconditioning phases of Group I; for this group, threshold and criterion were identical (as they are in the usual microswitch, bar-pressing apparatus). Accordingly, "100 per cent" of the emitted responses necessarily received reinforcement.[3] Upon going from reconditioning to shift, however, this group moved from a 2.5-gm. to a 16-gm. criterion, and—since threshold and criterion were no longer identical—circumstances permitted the animals to emit responses that did not meet criterion.

[3] With a threshold criterion the subjects display lever contacts falling below threshold, but the nature of "response" definition eliminates this behavior from measurement. Informal observation leads us to suspect that no matter how low a criterion is established, subcriterion behavior will be generated.

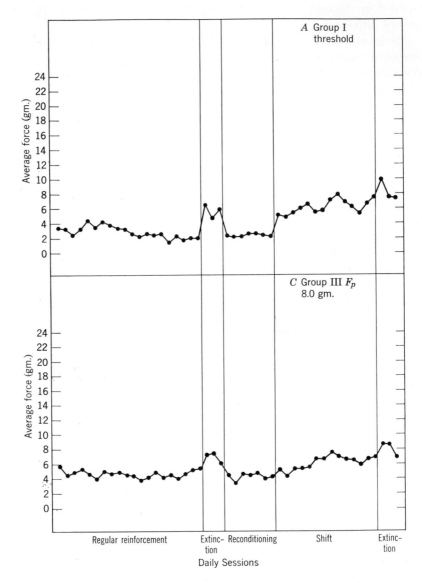

Figure 3-22   Average force of response (time integral of force divided by response duration) as a function of successive days for each of the groups. The average force for individual responses was computed, and means were taken for individual animals. The grand mean for each group is shown in the figure.

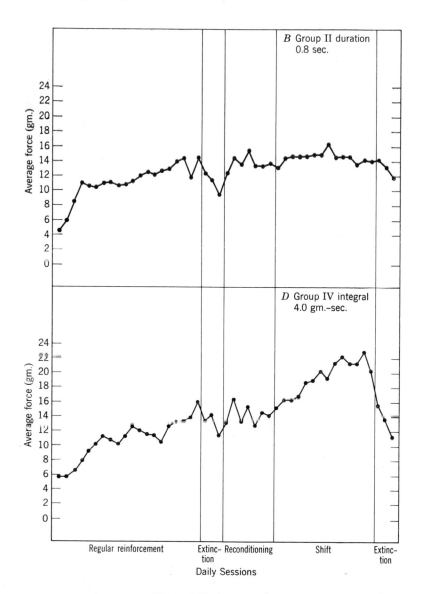

Figure 3-22   Continued.

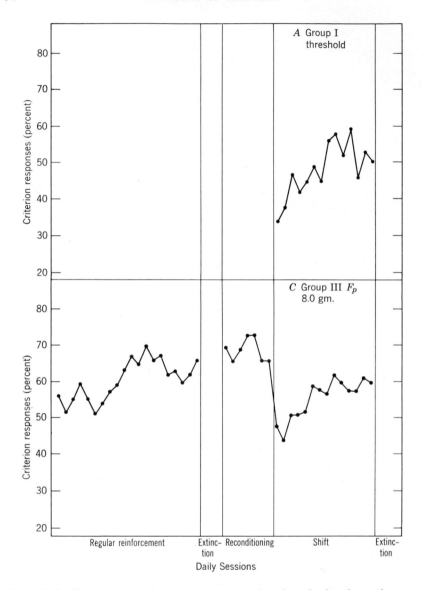

Figure 3-23 Mean percent of total responses meeting the criterion for each group as a function of successive days during the reinforced phases of the study. Conditioning and reconditioning data are omitted for Group I, since the response threshold and the reinforcement criterion were identical (that is, 100% of the responses necessarily met criterion).

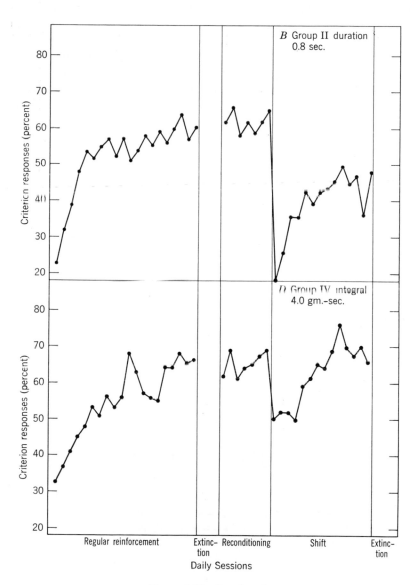

Figure 3-23   Continued.

For Groups II, III, and IV the percentage of criterion responses on the last day of regular reinforcement were—as the graph indicates—60.3 per cent, 66.4 per cent, and 65.6 per cent, respectively. These are mean percentages, based in each group on the performance of all six animals. On the last day of reconditioning, the percentages for the groups were, in order: 64.6 per cent, 65.5 per cent, and 68.5 per cent.

The data seem to be fairly conclusive. Despite the wide disparity in criteria (8.0 gm., 0.8 second, and 4.0 gram-seconds), the subjects' performances resulted in reinforcement of approximately 65 per cent of the responses. Figure 3-24 superposes the data for Groups II, III, and IV during all of conditioning, making visual comparison more direct. In conventional terminology, it shows that despite the availability (given adequate response magnitude and/or precision) of 100 per cent reinforcement, the subjects effectively placed themselves on a variable ratio schedule resulting in about 65 per cent reinforcement.

Could this be merely a coincidence, reflecting a peculiar (albeit inadvertent) selection of criteria that happened to be "matched" across response properties? We think not and for this simple reason. On the last day of reconditioning (the session reflecting the greatest amount of training at a given criterion), Group II (0.8-second duration criterion) was pressing with a mean peak force of 50.2 gm. (see Fig. 3-7-*A*). For the same session, Group III (8.0-gm. force criterion) was pressing

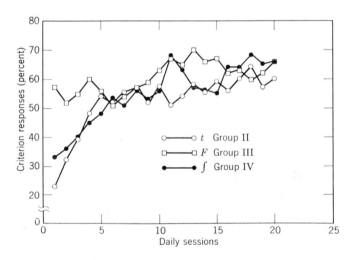

Figure 3-24 Mean per cent of total responses meeting the criterion for Groups II, III, and IV during initial conditioning.

at a level of only 12.7 gm. (Fig. 3-11-*A*). The groups were almost identical in their percentage of "success"—64.6 per cent versus 65.5 per cent. Apparently, it was not a matter of Group III's inability to go beyond the 12.7-gm. (and 65.5%) level, since Group II, composed of animals drawn from the same parent population, was roughly four times as high in force emission.

Based on the data discussed thus far, it seems reasonable to conclude that—over a wide range of criteria—the laboratory animals used in this series of studies differentiated their responses up to the point at which some 65 per cent of their responses were reinforced. One might make the generalization that behavior becomes stabilized at about this proportion of reinforced-to-total responses.

We would expect, however, that there are limitations to this generalization. Any of the reinforcement criteria used could be raised to a value so high that we would essentially place the animal in extinction. In other words, the subjects could go from 65 per cent of criterion "success" to zero and in time presumably cease responding altogether. Is it possible to raise the criteria to values that would result in the animals' stabilization at some percentage of "success" falling between 65 per cent and zero? Or is it an either-or issue—either the animal stabilizes at 65 per cent or he extinguishes? We may look to the shift data for some information on this question, since the shift criteria are raised to twice their respective values in reconditioning.

For the last day of shift (Fig. 3-23), the percentages for the groups previously considered are 48.3, 59.2, and 64.8. These values are significantly $(0.05 > p > 0.02)$ lower than for the last day of reconditioning as indicated by Wilcoxon's Paired Replicates Test (the 18 reconditioning percentages compared with the shift percentages for the same animals). However, despite the greater differences between group mean percentages than was characteristic of the reconditioning data, these intergroup differences are not, taken collectively, statistically reliable (Wilcoxon's Chi-Square Test for different treatments applied to the last day of shift data for all four groups). If, despite the rejection of over-all intergroup differences, Group IV (64.8%) is compared alternately with Group II (48.3%) and with Group I (51.0%), the differences are acceptable at $0.05 > p > 0.02$ in each case (Wilcoxon's Unpaired Replicates).

Taking these shift results into account, one sees that the question raised earlier may be answered in the affirmative—response stabilization *can* occur at percentages of "success" lower than 65 per cent. However, the remarkable consistency of the 65 per cent value during conditioning and reconditioning cannot be regarded lightly. Unfortunately, we have no additional data concerning the degree to which effort expenditure and discriminative capacities relate to these findings.

Time Integral of Force

It was argued in Chapter 1 that the time integral of force was closely related during active responding to energy conversion within the organism. This must remain an assumption until the necessary calorimetric validation procedures are performed.

If one tentatively accepts the assumption pending this rather difficult verification procedure, then certain interesting observations may be made. For example, it is apparent from the graphs that the duration-criterion group (Group II) exerted more effort than any other group during all phases of the experiment. As noted in the discussion of this group's performance (p. 29), apart from being differentiated in terms of response duration to levels well above the level of any other group (see Fig. 3-7-B), Group II animals also emitted peak forces exceeded only by Group IV. In fact, the position was taken that it is the feedback from force emissions that permits duration differentiation to take place. But whether or not this conjecture is correct, the empirical fact remains that Group II exerted the greatest amount of effort, as herein defined.

Given this observation, one wonders whether the previously remarked Group II decrease in the percentage of responses that attained criterion following shift is a related phenomenon. One might speculate that Group II was least "successful" (48.3% on the last day of shift) because it exerted the greatest effort in meeting its criterion (a mean of 25.6 gram-seconds). Although this speculation seems, at first blush, reasonable, its appeal is diminished when one observes that the *most* "successful" group (Group IV, 64.8%) emitted the second greatest effort (15.8 gram-seconds, followed by Group I, 5.3 gram-seconds; and Group III, 4.6 gram-seconds).

In general, although there is evidence that effort plays a role in the differentiation of responses, it is apparent that the stage is not left to effort alone. The influence of reinforcement contingencies (both past and current) and of discrimination (both capacity and training) is such as to limit seriously the consequences of mere effort expenditure.

Chapter Four

Differentiation and Discrimination

RESULTS OF A BASIC experiment were discussed in terms of the "differentiation" process in the previous chapter. In this chapter we examine "differentiation" more closely by comparing its characteristics with those of the better-understood (or perhaps just more familiar) "discrimination" process. Although the term "stimulus discrimination" has been in the literature at least since Pavlov's students first described the Method of Contrasts (Belyakov, 1911), the term "response differentiation" is relatively new (Skinner, 1938).

Stimulus Discrimination

In its simplest form stimulus discrimination refers to the process by which an organism comes to make a specific response to one stimulus (traditionally called the "positive stimulus") and to refrain from making the same response to another stimulus (the "negative stimulus"). In classical conditioning experiments these response tendencies can be measured in terms of magnitude; in instrumental conditioning experiments these tendencies are expressed in terms of the frequency of response occurrence. Regardless of the type of conditioning, however, and with the probable exception of Lashley and Wade (1946) and Razran (1949), there is wide agreement that discrimination takes place as follows (see Spence, 1937; Skinner, 1938; Hull, 1943, 1951): reinforcement of a response following presentation of the positive stimulus increases the strength of the response to this stimulus and in a decremental gradient to other stimuli lying along a continuum from the positive stimulus; nonreinforcement following the negative stimulus decreases the strength of the response to stimuli lying along a continuum from the negative stimulus in the same manner; accordingly, response strengths to positive and negative stimuli draw apart.

In the area of classical conditioning, experimental support for the foregoing observations is presumed (but not by Lashley and Wade or Razran) to derive from the work of Pavlov (1927), Bass and Hull (1934), Hovland (1937), and others.

The general applicability of this discrimination model to instrumental conditioning has been demonstrated by Frick (1948). Frick found that the key to the discrimination process lay in the strength of response in the presence of the negative stimulus (or S^Δ in Skinnerian terminology). He was able to show that rate of responding in the presence of S^Δ fell away in proportion to the disparity between the S^D (or positive stimulus) and S^Δ. S^D responding was not affected by the extent of the disparity between S^D and S^Δ.

Response Differentiation

It was noted earlier that the process of stimulus discrimination demands that a "specific response" characteristically comes to be made to a given stimulus. In point of fact, however, repetition of identical responses occurs but rarely. In bar pressing, for example, one response may be made with the left paw, another with the right; either of these responses, if it follows presentation of the positive stimulus, is reinforced. Similarly, one response may be of 3-gm., another of 30-gm. force. Variations in the form or magnitude of a response give rise to what Skinner calls subclasses of response. Through appropriate reinforcement, a particular subclass of response may be strengthened (this is "shaping"). In order to distinguish this process from sensory discrimination, Skinner coined the term "differentiation."

Superficially, it appears that with discrimination the stimuli are varied (usually alternated), and the response—when it occurs—is kept constant by the organism; with differentiation the stimuli remain the same, but the response is organismically varied. As Skinner put it in a key paragraph:

It is necessary to distinguish between the discrimination of stimuli and a process of differentiation between forms of response. The tendency to cast all behavior in the respondent mould, with the implication of a strict and ubiquitous stimulus-response relationship, is perhaps responsible for the neglect of this distinction in current work on discrimination. If for every response there were a rigorously corresponding stimulus, a discrimination between two forms of either term would necessarily involve the corresponding form of the other, and there would be no need to consider more than one process. But in operant behavior the strength of a response may be independently varied and two closely related forms of a response may become distinguished by developing different strengths irrespective of discriminated stimuli (p. 308, *ibid.*).

Granted that the use of a physiological, necessary and sufficient stimulus-response model to describe learned behavior is beset with misconceptions (see Chapter 1), we believe that the alternative suggested by Skinner—a "process" distinction between discrimination and differentiation—introduces additional difficulties. In the first place, this dichotomy implies to the unwary that although differentiation cannot be cast into the physiological *S-R* role, discrimination can. This was not, of course, suggested by Skinner and is simply not so; no generally accepted, present-day psychological theory contains this argument. In the second place, it is apparent that in at least one critical sense, response differentiation is operationally identical with stimulus discrimination: both phenomena are based upon appropriate strengthening and weakening of selected stimulus-response contingencies. This argues that not two, but one process is involved in differentiation and discrimination. We propose, therefore, that the distinction between discrimination and differentiation lies not in any difference in "process" but rather in the difference between the classes of discriminative stimuli cueing the organism's behavior. Discrimination, as it is conventionally understood, involves selective reinforcement of responses made to specific *exteroceptive* stimuli; differentiation, on the other hand, involves selective reinforcement of specific response characteristics, the appropriate values or forms of which are correlated with kinesthetic, cutaneous, or proprioceptive feedback stimuli.

The reasoning that leads to the supposition that organisms are capable of generating specific responses, only because they are capable of discriminating stimuli arising from the act of making the response itself, seems circular. On the other hand, it must be noted that it is the very behavior in question that is assumed to be "circular," inasmuch as it is described by means of a feedback model. The principal consequence of such a model, insofar as specific responding is concerned, is that there will be a lag between the instantaneous stimulus (and its time derivatives) and the ensuing increase or decrease in response value; the lag, in turn, would engender a tendency to overshoot or undershoot the particular response value reinforced. We would expect, however, that such variability should decrease with learning.

Following this line of thought, Notterman (1959) was led to conclude that response differentiation (or "internalized" stimulus discrimination) must take place in the ordinary bar-pressing situation, or else the animal would never learn to press the bar with at least the level of force required to close the microswitch. The results of the experiment reviewed in the previous chapter suggested that animals acquire a tendency to respond with forces somewhat above that force required for reinforcement (perhaps because "overshoots" but not "undershoots" are reinforced—see Chapter 5), and that the learning is characterized by a decrease in variability of force emission and closer conformity to the criterion for reinforcement.

These findings are consistent with the argument that differentiation utilizes the same process of selective reinforcement as does discrimination. An animal presses the bar with a 5-gm. force and thereby generates a pattern of cutaneous and kinesthetic stimuli. If the reinforcement criterion is 5 gm., then the animal's 5-gm. (or higher) response is reinforced. The correlated "motor" stimuli are thus in the position of acquiring an S^D (or "cueing") function for pressure release. Similarly, when the animal presses with less than a 5-gm. force, the pattern of stimuli accompanying the unreinforced response lies in an S^Δ reference. As a result, it is possible for the organism to learn to discriminate between force levels that are reinforced and those that are not.

Extending the argument further, it follows that in any bar-pressing experiment involving exteroceptive stimulus discrimination, actually *two* discriminations are involved. Not only must the animal learn to discriminate those motor-response cues associated with a given level (or higher) of force emission but also he must learn to discriminate the exteroceptive cues that, conjointly with a required level of force emission, determine whether a given response will be reinforced. Although research attention is usually given to the second of these two discriminative demands, the first has been virtually ignored.

Consider simple light-dark discrimination in bar pressing, with light the exteroceptive S^D (or S^{D_e}), and dark the exteroceptive S^Δ (or S^{Δ_e}). In accordance with our definitions of "threshold" and "criterion" (p. 17), assume that the force required to register as a response is 3 gm. and that the force required for reinforcement is 5 gm.[1] Hence, the internalized S^D (or S^{D_i}) consists of stimuli associated with forces of 5 gm. or higher, and the internalized S^Δ (or S^{Δ_i}) consists of stimuli

[1] A 3-gm. rather than a 2.5-gm. response threshold was used in the experiment reported in this chapter.

associated with forces below the 5-gm. criterion. (Of the $S^{\Delta i}$ forces, however, the only ones measured would lie between the 3-gm. threshold and the criterion.)

To provide a convenient indication of the feedback loop in the generation of motor-response discriminative stimuli, we shall use the following symbol:

$$R \longrightarrow S^{D_i}$$

The loop should be taken to indicate that S^{D_i} changes in time as a function of R and that the mechanism consists of afferent and efferent neural connections. Behaviorally, it follows that expression 1 represents the only circumstance in which reinforcement is received during the establishment of a "yes-no" discrimination:

$$S^{D_e} \longrightarrow R \longrightarrow S^{D_i} \longrightarrow S^R \tag{1}$$

In a specific light-dark discrimination, expression 1 states that the organism received positive reinforcement in the presence of the light and for emitted forces above some designated force criterion. Expression 2 says that the animal responded during the light condition but did not meet the force criterion and was unreinforced:

$$S^{D_e} \longrightarrow R \longrightarrow S^{\Delta_i} \not\longrightarrow S^R \tag{2}$$

Expression 3 indicates that an animal met the force requirement but did so in the dark and received no reinforcement. And expression 4 describes an animal that met neither exteroceptive nor internalized conditions.

$$S^{\Delta_e} \longrightarrow R \longrightarrow S^{D_i} \not\longrightarrow S^R \tag{3}$$

$$S^{\Delta_e} \longrightarrow R \longrightarrow S^{\Delta_i} \not\longrightarrow S^R \tag{4}$$

Although the conventional bar-pressing apparatus (one activated by a microswitch) does not permit measurement of forces, it does inform the experimenter of the occurrence of S^{D_i} responses, that is, any and all responses that close the microswitch. But the recording of neither the occurrence nor—consequently—the measurement of $S^{\Delta i}$ responses is possible.

With the present system, both measurement and enumeration of S^{Di} responses are possible. However, if the recording threshold and reinforcement criterion are made to coincide, then $S^{\Delta i}$ responses cannot be included in the data gathered. The $S^{\Delta i}$ response may only be sampled through separation of the criterion from the threshold. The distribution curves of the preceding chapter describe data of this sort for Groups II, III, and IV during acquisition.

In terms of the foregoing discussion, then, the consequences of expressions 2 and 4 cannot be examined in the conventional apparatus, and—depending upon the coincidence of threshold and criterion—may not be examinable in the present system. Moreover, since the conventional apparatus can sense the occurrence of S^{Di} but not the magnitude of the related forces, its usefulness for expressions 1 and 3 is limited.

Relating this analysis to earlier work in the literature, it is clear that Frick's (1948) study was concerned with the consequences of expressions 1 and 3 but only as to rate of response. The additional measurement of force in this situation has the following implications: to be parallel with the Frick study, response threshold and reinforcement criterion must coincide; this, in turn, means that $S^{\Delta i}$ responses, although they occur, can be neither counted nor measured, and therefore cannot be examined; S^{Di} responses, however, can be counted (as Frick did) and measured as well.

Preliminary work directed at the suggested force analysis during discriminations has been reported (Notterman and Block, 1960). This pilot experiment essentially replicated Frick's research but only at a single value (the maximum) of $S^{De}-S^{\Delta e}$ disparity. The study described in this chapter examines both rate and force effects for several values of $S^{De}-S^{\Delta e}$ disparity and extends the analysis to include response-by-response sequential force emissions.[2]

It is precisely because of the extension to force measurement that the structure of Frick's earlier study has been largely replicated. In this sense, the Frick experiment serves as a control with the function of assuring us that our analysis of force effects is in the context of information paralleling conventional rate data and is not the conse-

[2] The experiment reported in this chapter was conducted by A. H. Block as a portion of his doctoral dissertation, Princeton University, 1960.

quence of departures from previous experimental procedures. Moreover, it should also be noted that the experiment described in the following pages is not offered as a test of the loop notions comprising expressions 1 through 4 (some evidence bearing on these issues is presented in Chapter 7). Rather, this experiment is seen as providing within the context of the preceding discussions some clarification of the role of magnitude measures of behavior in operant discrimination processes, a role that—if not carefully examined—may be confused with magnitude measures in the application of the Method of Contrasts in Pavlovian conditioning. Considered in this light, the experiment reported in this chapter is largely of methodological, and perhaps theoretical, interest. It bears on the continuing inquiry as to whether various behavioral characteristics attributed exclusively to either classical or instrumental types of learning are actually inherent in the type of conditioning examined or merely derived from the type of measure employed. Noteworthy in the present context is the necessary description of generalization and discrimination data in terms of response magnitude when classical behavior is involved. As to instrumental procedures, generalization and discrimination phenomena during bar pressing have not heretofore been studied by means of magnitude measures, although this is operationally possible.

Method

Both S^{De} and $S^{\Delta e}$ consisted of the illumination level in the modified Skinner box, measured in foot-candles. Two lamp bases were mounted on one wall of an aluminum container, the floor of which consisted of opal diffusing glass. General Electric 15-watt/110-volt bulbs were measured with the use of a Macbeth Illuminometer; two of equal brightness were obtained. Small rectangular boxes with photographic-filter holders at one end were mounted below the lamp bases. The entire unit was placed directly over the transparent plastic top of the experimental cage when an animal was being run. The illumination from one lamp was approximately 20 foot-candles at a point on the floor of the cage directly in front of the bar. For all animals, the S^{De} was held constant at 20 foot-candles. $S^{\Delta e}$ for the experimental groups was provided by placing one of several Wratten neutral density filters in the other slide holder to achieve the necessary differences in illumination. The values serving as $S^{\Delta e}$ were 10, 7.5, 2, and 0 foot-candles. The control group saw no change in illumination (20 foot-candles remained constant during the experiment) but was permitted to obtain reinforcement on the same time schedule as the other animals.

A variable interval timer determined the duration of the positive and negative (Method of Contrast) visual stimuli. To preclude any possible temporal discrimination, the daily presentations of S^{De} and $S^{\Delta e}$ consisted of time periods having the following irregular duration and sequence: 80 seconds of S^D, 80 of S^Δ, 40 S^D, 20 S^Δ, 20 S^D, 160 S^Δ, 10 S^D, 40 S^Δ, 160 S^D, and 10 S^Δ. This sequence was programmed on a continuous tape permitting daily sessions to begin at any point in the schedule and run either forward or backward. A daily experimental session consisted of two entire sequences using a total of 20 minutes and 40 seconds per animal.

Four animals were assigned to each of five groups, which were designated according to the ratio of S^Δ illumination to S^D: Group I, 100 per cent; Group II, 50 per cent; Group III, 37.5 per cent; Group IV, 10 per cent; and Group V, 0 per cent. (Early in the experiment, one animal from Group III and one from Group IV died of respiratory illness, reducing these groups to three animals each.)

The three phases of the procedure follow.

Operant Level

Preconditioning response rates were taken for all animals over seven successive sessions. The schedule of presentation of the positive and negative stimuli was in effect, that is, response rates were obtained in the presence of the stimuli that later were to become S^D and S^Δ.[3]

Discrimination Training

For the next 16 days, the animals were run on the previously specified S^D–S^Δ schedule. In the presence of S^D all responses at or above a 3-gm. criterion were reinforced. (For Group I, reinforcement was available only during those time periods when S^D was in effect for the other groups.) Under S^Δ illumination, no responses were reinforced.

Extinction

Extinction conditions (seven sessions) paralleled those of operant level.

[3] Whenever S^D and S^Δ appear without subscript, the exteroceptive condition (S^{De} or $S^{\Delta e}$) is indicated.

Results and Discussion

The major results of this study are shown in Figs. 4-1 to 4-7. The graphs give mean peak force and mean rate of responding as a function of group S^D–S^Δ disparity for operant level, session 1; discrimination, sessions 1, 3, 5, and 16; and extinction, sessions 1 and 7. Comment follows the same sequential order.

Figure 4-1 indicates that no systematic preconditioning effect was

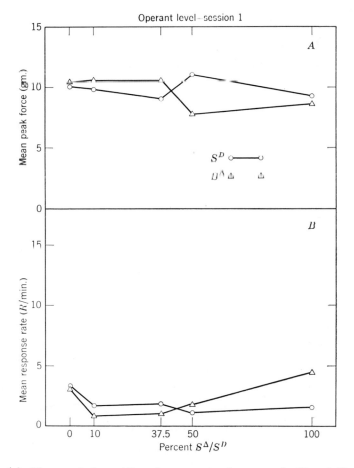

Figure 4-1   Mean peak force (A) and mean rate of response in S^D and S^Δ (B) on the first day of operant level as a function of the ratio of the stimulus intensities. Data are group means.

produced by the variations in illumination; none of the differences in peak force or rate of response between S^D and S^Δ is significant. In Fig. 4-2, the initial effects of S^Δ extinction appear in an over-all tendency of both rate and force measures to be higher for S^Δ than for S^D. By session 3 of discrimination (Fig. 4-3), all groups emitted forces higher in S^Δ than in S^D, a phenomenon that persisted throughout the remain-

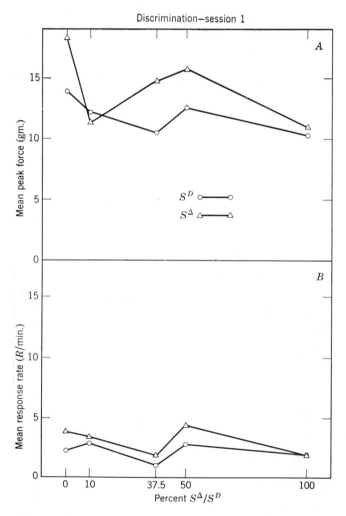

Figure 4-2 Mean peak force (*A*) and mean rate of response in S^D and S^Δ (*B*) on the first day of discrimination training as a function of the ratio of the stimulus intensities. Data reflect group means.

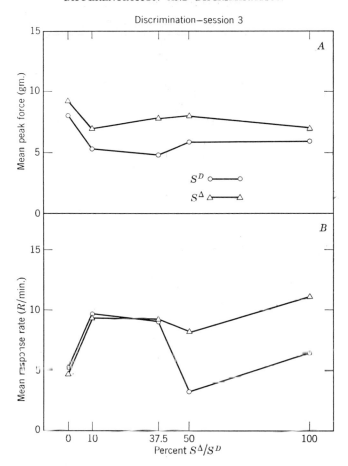

Figure 4-3 Mean peak force (*A*) and mean rate of response in S^D and S^Δ (*B*) on the third day of discrimination training as a function of the ratio of the stimulus intensities. Data reflect group means.

ing discrimination sessions; rate measures, however, were still not stabilized. The data for session 5 (Fig. 4-4) reveal similar characteristics; in fact, it was not until session 12 (not shown) that all the experimental groups generated S^Δ rates that were lower than rates for S^D. The last discrimination session (Fig. 4-5) reflected the stabilization consequences of the discrimination procedure. In rate of emission, S^D levels were fairly constant from group to group. The S^Δ points, however, yielded a function that increased with decreasing S^D–S^Δ disparity; that is, the closer the S^D–S^Δ brightness, the greater the tendency for

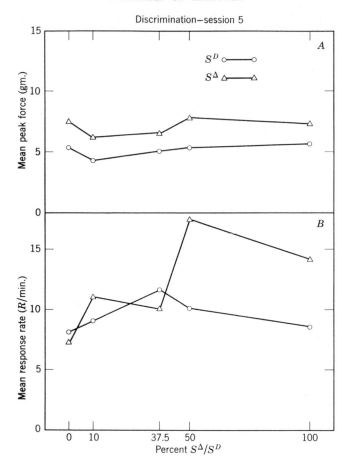

Figure 4-4   Mean peak force (*A*) and mean rate of response in S^D and S^Δ (*B*) on the fifth day of discrimination training as a function of the ratio of the stimulus intensities. Data reflect group means.

S^Δ rate of responding to approach the rate of S^D. The limiting case in which S^Δ brightness was equal to S^D brightness (Group I, 100% S^Δ/S^D), showed approximately equal S^D and S^Δ rates (the observed difference is not significant).

Although the animals in this experiment had far more training than did Frick's animals, Fig. 4-5 indicates marked similarity of the shape of the S^Δ curve to that reported by Frick (1948). The primary divergence between the two sets of data occurs in the 50 per cent group. Frick found that his 50 per cent group did not differ from his "periodic-reinforcement" (control) group; the present data reveal that a significantly lower S^Δ rate was produced by the 50 per cent than by the 100 per cent group. One explanation of this difference may relate to the greater amount of training given in the current study. The two sets of data are in accord in finding that the S^D rate of response is approximately equal from group to group.

Turning to the force data of Fig. 4-5, one sees that the S^Δ forces, although consistently higher than S^D from group to group, show no systematic relationship to the S^Δ/S^D brightness ratio. Of major interest

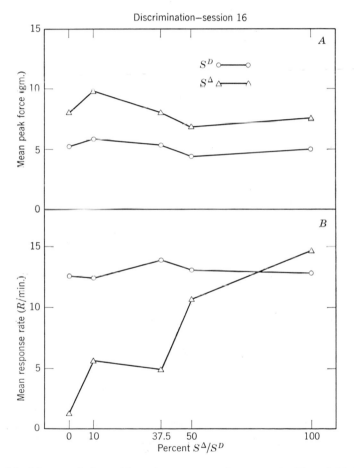

Figure 4-5 Mean peak force (A) and mean rate of response in S^D and S^Δ (B) on the 16th day of discrimination training as a function of the ratio of the stimulus intensities. Data reflect group means.

is the question of why rate of response was related to S^Δ/S^D disparity, but force of response was not. Discussion of this question must await examination of the extinction and "sequential-analysis" data.

The extinction data (Figs. 4-6 and 4-7) show that the S^Δ rate of response continued to be lower than the rate for S^D, even though both S^Δ and S^D rates were decreasing; for the first session of extinction, the S^D rate paralleled the S^Δ function characteristic of discrimination session 16. The force levels for the first day of extinction were all higher than corresponding points for the last discrimination session *but the*

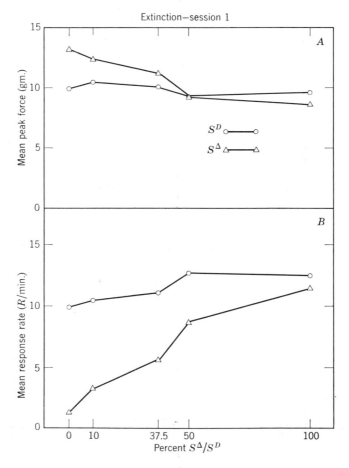

Figure 4-6   Mean peak force (*A*) and mean rate of response in S^D and S^Δ (*B*) on the first day of extinction as a function of the ratio of the stimulus intensities. Data reflect group means.

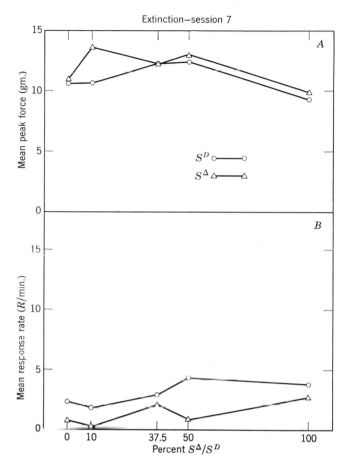

Figure 4-7 Mean peak force (A) and mean rate of response in S^D and S^Δ (B) on the seventh day of extinction as a function of the ratio of the stimulus intensities. Data reflect group means.

S^D forces consistently increased more than S^Δ forces. This S^D increase was great enough on extinction 1 to approach S^Δ values, and, indeed, exceed them (nonsignificantly) in Group I. The force levels and also the rate data appear by extinction 7 (Fig. 4-7) to be approaching that of operant level 1 (Fig. 4-1).

A "limited-sequence" analysis was made of successive force emissions during the last day of discrimination training. It will be recalled that for each experimental session the subjects were exposed to an irregular sequence of S^D and S^Δ periods. The effect of transition from one exteroceptive condition to another was examined by observing the force of the last response made prior to each stimulus change and the force of each of the first five responses made in the "new" condition. Means for each step in the sequence were computed by combining the data for all of the animals in each group. The means for the experimental groups (differences between S^D and S^Δ) were not reliably different from each other, nor did any consistent trends appear. Accordingly, the data for (experimental) Groups II through V were combined and labeled "Experimental" (solid symbols) in Fig. 4-8. The open circles (S^D) and the open triangles (S^Δ) are for (control) Group I, for which there never was any stimulus change.

The left side of Fig. 4-8 indicates that, for the experimental groups, the first response after S^D presentation (and *before* reinforcement) was strikingly lower than the force characteristic of the prior S^Δ response. The observed drop in force was significant beyond the 0.01 level; all

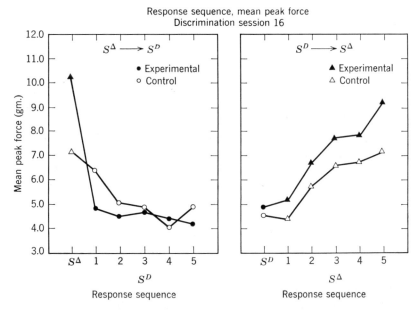

Figure 4-8   Mean peak force of response as a function of successive responses for transitions from S^Δ to S^D, and S^D to S^Δ. The last response preceding a stimulus change and the initial five responses in the new stimulus are shown. Data reflect group means on the 16th day of discrimination training. The "control" group represents those animals for which there was no difference in the exteroceptive stimulus between S^D and S^Δ.

14 experimental animals showed this. Although the control group also showed a drop, it was much less than for the experimental groups and not close to reliability (in fact, two of the four control animals actually increased in force).

In going from S^D to S^Δ (right side of graph), one sees a drift by both experimental and control animals toward increase in force emission; this gradual shift did not manifest itself, however, until *after* the first unreinforced response in S^Δ.

The evidence is reasonably clear. The experimental animals adjusted force levels immediately upon presentation of S^D (and prior to reinforcement); the converse did not occur. In going from S^D to S^Δ, the observed increase in force appears to be a gradual one, occurring after nonreinforcement.

The empirical findings of this study pose three problems: (1) Why is it that after the discrimination is established, the disparity between S^D and S^Δ rates varies with positive-negative stimulus difference, but no such systematic effect appears as to force? (2) Why is it that, although invariant with S^D–S^Δ stimulus difference, S^Δ force is consistently higher than S^D force? (3) Why is it that, for the experimental groups, force level drops immediately upon S^Δ change to S^D, but the converse does not occur?

In dealing with these specific questions, we shall have opportunity to refer to the discrimination-differentiation paradigms (expressions) described earlier in this chapter and to comment upon certain operational difficulties involved in the gathering of generalization curves.

1. *Force Invariant with S^D–S^Δ Disparity.* The key to this problem lies in the question: What is the organism being reinforced to do (or to discriminate) with respect to rate and with respect to force of response?

RATE. During the presentation of S^D, all animals, regardless of group, are reinforced for pressing as often as they can. The limiting condition eventually turns out to be how rapidly they can eat the pellets with which they are reinforced (see Frick, 1948). This accounts for high and constant S^D rate from group to group.

Variation in S^Δ rate is responsible for S^D–S^Δ rate disparity. The animals are never reinforced for any S^Δ value, but the closer S^Δ is to S^D (that is, as we go from left to right on the abscissa of the discrimination figures), the more the inherent discriminative capacity of the organism is taxed. In a sense, the situation is paralleled by the Method of Constant Stimuli in human psychophysics. The closer the compari-

son stimulus is to the standard, the greater is the number of "no-difference" judgments made by the subject. According to this analogy,
the S^Δ rate curve in Fig. 4-7 is essentially a "percentage-of-no-differ-
ence" curve in a psychophysical context. Thus, the S^D–S^Δ rate function owes its existence to the increase in "no-difference" responses as
the S^Δ (or "comparison") stimulus approaches in value the S^D (or
"standard") stimulus.

FORCE. The animals are reinforced during presentation of S^D for
emitting a response above a criterion level, which was 3 gm. in this
experiment (see expression 1). This requirement is the same for all
groups, regardless of exteroceptive S^D–S^Δ stimulus disparity. If the organism responds during S^Δ because of failure to discriminate between
S^D and S^Δ, there is no reason to expect this response to be any different in magnitude from those emitted during S^D. According to this
analysis, the consequence of increasing the similarity between exteroceptive S^Δ and S^D should be manifested, not in any corresponding increase or decrease in S^Δ response magnitude but only in an increase
in the occurrence of S^Δ responses. In point of fact, the S^Δ rate data
conform with what this model predicts; the S^Δ force data, however,
instead of being equal in magnitude with the S^D, are consistently
higher but—again in accordance with the model—not in any manner
related to S^Δ stimulus value. We shall return to this apparent anomaly
shortly.

The student of generalization phenomena will no doubt be reminded by these remarks of an argument made by Lashley and Wade
(1946) in their well-known critique of Pavlovian generalization theory.
They stated: "The gradient of habit strength is a product of *variable
stimulus thresholds,* not of spread of associative processes." (Italics
ours.) The parallel we have drawn with the Method of Constant
Stimuli certainly presents a similar view. However, despite the reas-
surance that comes of relating current findings to a position taken
more than 15 years ago, we believe that the experimental evidence
offered by Lashley and Wade suffers from the same limitations as
ours—it is highly questionable whether generalization data gathered
by means of operant behavior can be used to examine the generalization of Pavlovian responses. Although Lashley and Wade made no
such distinction, we must argue that the question of the existence of
Pavlovian generalization can be settled only by examination of relevant classical conditioning procedures. While we believe we can account for our gradient by taking recourse to fairly straightforward

discrimination paradigms, an extension to Pavlovian behavior is beset with the dangers of superficial resemblance.

2. S^Δ *Force Consistently Higher than* S^D *Force.* According to our Method-of-Constant-Stimuli analogy, we should expect no difference in force level during S^Δ compared with that emitted during S^D. But in fact, S^Δ is consistently higher than S^D, and we are here concerned with an understanding of this phenomenon.

In one sense, the explanation is quite simple: S^Δ is a nonreinforced condition. We have already observed (Chapter 3) that forces become higher during extinction. Since S^Δ constitutes an exposure to extinction operations, it is not surprising to find that response forces become elevated. The random cycles of S^D and S^Δ constitute successive reconditioning and extinction.

In another sense, however, this account begs the question. The fundamental issue is this: Why does response force rise in the first place during nonreinforcement? Our speculations upon this issue, together with a description of some experimental procedures designed to test these speculations, comprise the next chapter.

3. S^D *Control of Force Level.* The problem we are concerned with here is that the response-sequence analysis (Fig. 4-8) shows that, for the experimental groups, force level drops immediately upon the change from S^Δ to S^D, but there is no corresponding, immediate shift in changing from S^D to S^Δ.

Turning to the left side of Fig. 4-8, one should note that the difference between experimental and control groups in magnitude of the last response in S^Δ is not at all reliable. For the experimental groups, however, as observed previously, the drop in force from the last S^Δ response to the first S^D response is quite significant ($p < .001$), because each of the 14 animals showed this downward shift. The corresponding comparison for the control group is not significant; these animals were evenly divided in the direction of shift.

There seems little doubt that the exteroceptive cue provided by the change from S^Δ to S^D signals (for the experimental groups) a resumption of S^D rate of responding and at lower forces. It is equally certain that the cue provided by the change from S^D to S^Δ does not initiate an immediate rise to higher forces. What it does initiate is a drop in response rate and in a manner related inversely to the degree of similarity between S^Δ and S^D (see Fig. 4-5-B). Again, the analogy with the Method of Constant Stimuli suggests itself. The experimental animals tend not to respond in S^Δ; when they do, it is in proportion to the similarity between the "standard" (S^D) and the "comparison" (S^Δ) and is executed with—initially—the same force as that characteristic of S^D responses. However, as the animal (experimental *or* control) responds and goes unreinforced, the "extinction effect" becomes evident (right side of Fig. 4-8), that is, forces become elevated. Here again, we confront the problem of why it is that forces become higher during runs of nonreinforcement. We now turn our attention to this issue.

Chapter Five

Extinction Theories and Band Discrimination

FORCE OF RESPONSE tends to rise during S^Δ, it was observed in the preceding chapter. This phenomenon was related to the extinction operations inherent in S^Δ, because, as noted in Chapter 3, response magnitude increases during extinction. We are now concerned with the origin of the force increase during nonreinforcement—why do forces rise in the first place?

In considering this problem, we find it convenient to dichotomize suggested explanations into two groups, biological and learning. We shall briefly examine various theories in these two categories, bearing in mind that they may not be mutually exclusive.

Biological

One can account for increased force during nonreinforcement by asserting that such behavior is a consequence of natural selection. One can argue that the presence of gravity has provided us with a physical environment in which greater expenditures of energy (or more vigorous responses) following nonreinforcement often result in eventual reinforcement. The squirrel dragging a nut to its nest, the dog giving chase to a fleet rabbit, the farmer lifting a hundred-pound bag of oats—all may increase the probability of success by exerting more energy (following initial failure), a phenomenon traceable to physical, inertial characteristics that owe their existence to gravitation. It is at least conceivable, then, that the behavioral phenomenon of exerting additional force following nonreinforcement is a biological trait resulting from the process of genetic selection.

"Frustration" or "activation" theories of extinction effects probably belong to the biological classification, too, especially insofar as "frustration" is considered to be a "primary, aversive motivational condition . . ." (Amsel, 1958). From this viewpoint, the increase in vigor following nonreinforcement is regarded as a result of "frustration," which—in turn—is a convenient label for describing certain genetically established behavioral qualities that appear following nonreinforcement.

The "frustration" theories would also indicate a role for emotional responses in the general extinction pattern. A position of this sort was offered by Halasz (1963) when he commented on an earlier report of the study included in Chapter 9 (Mintz, 1962; 1963). Halasz suggested that the force elevations during runs of nonreinforced responses were mediated by emotional response patterns. In the particular Fixed-Ratio study in question, emotional mediation seemed unlikely. However, emotionality during extinction has been suggested by a number of learning theorists (Skinner, 1938; Keller and Schoenfeld, 1950), and the explanatory value of the concept deserves serious consideration.

Learning

In contrast to the biological theories, at least two explanations emphasize learning variables—explanations offered by Schoenfeld (1950a) and by Notterman and Block (1960). Antecedents to both of these may be found in Skinner (1938).

Schoenfeld proposes that the dimension of force is but one of several continua along which various subclasses of response may be specified. Thus, in the conventional bar-pressing situation the generic class of response is defined as any behavior by the organism that closes the microswitch component of the lever. Topographical subclasses of response, then, include left-paw presses, right-paw presses, chin presses, etc.

Similarly, all forces above the minimum force required to close the switch (what we would term "threshold") represent subclasses of response according to the actual force level emitted (for instance, 6 gm., 7 gm., 8 gm., etc.). Schoenfeld hypothesizes that a wide sampling of various response magnitudes (or "subclasses") is reinforced during the early stages of acquisition and that each of these subclasses must then be separately extinguished if response strength is to be reduced. It is for this reason that high forces (as well as low forces) are observed during extinction.

Goldberg (1959) tested this hypothesis by means of our apparatus.

He reasoned that if Schoenfeld's speculation was correct, the distribution of forces obtained during extinction should be similar to the distribution characteristic of acquisition. Figure 5-1 shows the type of comparison which Goldberg made. Note that the configuration of extinction is quite similar to that of acquisition. The data shown are for a single subject, trained on a 3-gm. threshold, with criterion identical to threshold.

While the Schoenfeld hypothesis was not contradicted by these findings, there is a nuance about the findings that suggests the need for further inquiry. If Fig. 5-1 is carefully examined, it will be observed that the right (or "high-force") tail of the extinction distribution lies above that of the acquisition distribution. This is true for each of the

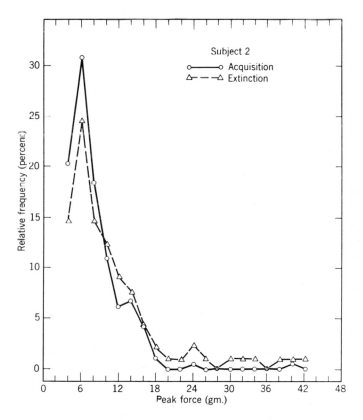

Figure 5-1   Relative frequency distributions of peak force of response for a single animal during acquisition and subsequent extinction. The reinforcement criterion was 3-gm. peak force.

nine subjects used in the study. We confront again, empirically, the rise of forces during extinction, only now we can say that they rise *more* than is accounted for by the original acquisition distribution of forces, despite the correlation that Goldberg demonstrated between the acquisition and extinction distributions of forces.

The approach taken by Notterman and Block (1960)—although of a frankly learning-theory variety—begins with the same observations that characterize the "natural-selection" or "frustration" hypotheses, that is, the self-evident importance of gravitational attraction in shaping behavior. It is argued that biological organisms are exposed from birth to reinforcement contingencies in which successively more vigorous responding tends to produce reinforcement. The rat presses the bar but the switch does not close; if he happens to press harder, the switch closes, and he gets reinforced. If he had pressed the second time with less force, he again would have gone unreinforced. Thus, in such behavioral situations, the organism may incidentally learn that an increase in vigor of response following nonreinforcement tends to increase the probability of reinforcement.

While the Schoenfeld explanation emphasizes the static and almost permanent nature of reinforced subclasses of response, the Notterman and Block speculation calls attention to the adventitious or incidental directional aspects of reinforcement—generally in the direction of emission of higher forces. While the biological theories emphasize natural or species endowment, the Notterman and Block argument is couched in learning-theory terms. Interestingly enough, none of these diverse "solutions" to the question of higher forces during extinction is incompatible with any other. It is entirely possible that all these alternatives are involved to some greater or lesser extent. The determination of whether the incidental-directional-reinforcement (IDR) explanation can survive experimental test is the subject of inquiry of the experiment described in this chapter. The reasoning leading to this experiment was as follows: if a group of animals were conditioned at an 8-gm. criterion and then extinguished, we would expect the previously described stabilization of force during acquisition (see Chapter 3) and the commonly observed increase in force during extinction.

Given these findings alone, any one of the biological or learning-theory explanations could account for the data. Suppose, however, a second group of animals were run, one with an upper limit (for example, 16 gm.) as well as a lower limit (8 gm.). A subject in the second group must press above 8 gm., but not higher than 16 gm., in order to obtain reinforcement. The consequence of such a "band"—

according to the IDR notion—should be to create a situation in which the animal is exposed to bidirectional reinforcement contingencies: occasionally it will press below 8 gm. and be reinforced for pressing harder during consequent responding; occasionally it will press above 16 gm. and be reinforced for pressing with less vigor in succeeding responses. It should therefore follow that, as compared with the 8-gm. criterion group, extinction would generate a shift to *lower* forces (below 8 gm.) as well as the usual shift to higher forces (above 16 gm.). Of course, a rigid interpretation of the "frustration" explanation would lead one to disregard the directional-learning aspects entirely. But it is altogether likely that such an interpretation is unnecessarily constraining—there is nothing about the biological explanation that precludes the existence of learning effects.

With the addition of still a third group, a direct comparison may be made between the predictive value of the Schoenfeld-Goldberg hypothesis and that of the Notterman-Block speculation. This confrontation requires that the subjects first be trained on a 4-to-16-gm. band and then be switched to an 8-to-16-gm. band, prior to extinction. It would follow from the "response-subclass" argument that extinction of the initially 4-to-16-gm. group should see the generation of relatively more low forces than would be expected from the extinction of the initially 8-to-16-gm. group. On the other hand, the IDR explanation would have to predict relatively *higher* forces during extinction for the initially 4-to-16-gm. group, since these animals have experienced a raising of the lower limit from 4 gm. to 8 gm., and have thus been exposed to an additional requirement to "press harder."

Procedure

The procedure followed in this experiment reflected the discussion of the preceding pages. Six animals were assigned to each of three groups. Group I was exposed to 20 sessions of 8-to-16-gm. "band" reinforcement, as previously explained. Animals in this group, as well as the others, were permitted to obtain 50 pellets per session under regular reinforcement of criterion responses. Group II was placed initially on a 4-to-16-gm. band for seven sessions and then shifted to an 8-to-16-gm. band for an additional 13 sessions. Group III was kept on an 8-gm. criterion (no upper limit) for all 20 sessions. For each group, extinction was initiated at the first session following the 20th day of acquisition. Three 10-minute sessions were devoted to extinction.

Results and Discussion

The principal results of this experiment are shown in Fig. 5-2. Since the band groups (Groups I and II) were placed on this reinforcement contingency without preliminary training, there were instances of irregularities during the first day of acquisition, such as removal of animals from the experimental box if response frequency dropped to marginal values and return of these animals after a lapse of several hours. Consequently, data were not gathered for the first session. For convenience in reading the graph and interpreting the data, the upper and lower band limits for Groups I and II are indicated by the horizontal lines. The points shown for Group II are based on five animals, because one animal died during the course of the experiment. Note that the mean peak force for the six animals comprising Group I tended to be quite stable over the 20 acquisition sessions and consistently remained within the 8-to-16-gm. requirement. The perturbations of Group II can be rationalized in the following way. Since the first seven sessions for this group involved a 4-to-16-gm. band, it would be expected that, by the seventh acquisition session,

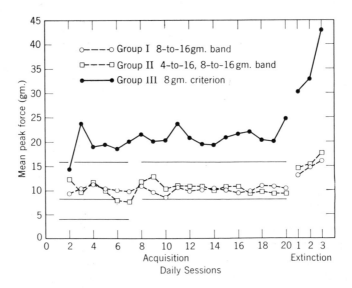

Figure 5-2 Mean peak force of response as a function of successive days during acquisition and extinction for all three groups.

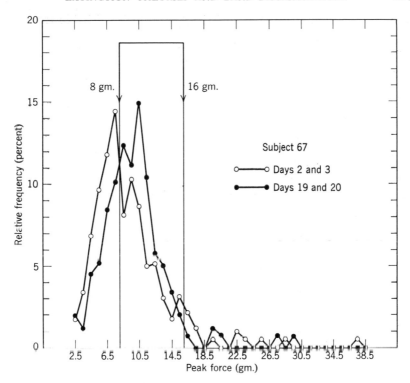

Figure 5-3 Relative frequency distributions of peak force of response for a single animal during the early and final stages of training with an 8-to-16 gm. peak-force band criterion.

Group II's mean peak force should be lower than that of Group I. The graph does, indeed, indicate that Group II was lower than Group I on sessions 6 and 7, but the difference is—by two-tailed test (Wilcoxon's Non-Parametric)—not significant at the 0.05 level. (However, by one-tailed test, an argument for the use of which is possibly tenable, the observed differences are significant between the 0.05 and 0.02 levels of confidence.)

In going from session 7 to session 8, Group II encountered the 8-to-16-gm. band for the first time. We would expect, since reinforcement was then withheld for responses in the 4-to-8-gm. range, that the force level should rise, and—in fact—each of the six animals showed the expected increase. After the initial increase, and probably as a consequence of being on the same band, Group II's mean peak force became stabilized at a value statistically nondistinguishable from that of Group I.

The comparison deserving comment is between Group I and Group III. (Group III will be recognized as similar to Group II, Chapter 3, in that identical criteria were employed. The 8-gm. criterion group reported here was somewhat higher in mean peak force than the group previously described.) It may be seen from Group I's data that the principal consequence of having an upper (16-gm.) as well as lower (8-gm.) criterion is reduction of emitted force levels by approximately one half in comparison with Group III (10 gm. versus 20 gm.).

A clearer conception of the role played by discriminative (or differentiating) processes during band-reinforcement contingencies is offered in Fig. 5-3. This graph gives the relative frequencies of force levels for a single subject during the course of acquisition. The observed shift in the peak of the distribution is characteristic of what we have come to call "band discrimination." The difference in frequency distribution between days 2 and 3 and days 19 and 20 is significant beyond the 0.01 level by the Kolmogorov-Smirnov test. For this particular subject, 45 per cent of his responses (threshold was at 2.5 gm., as customary) fell within the criterion band on days 2 and 3. By the 19th and 20th sessions, 65 per cent of the responses met the criterion. Performance by the group as a whole, however, was somewhat less "successful." Figure 5-4 suggests an asymptote at approximately 50 per cent. As we suggested in Chapter 3, p. 73, it seems rea-

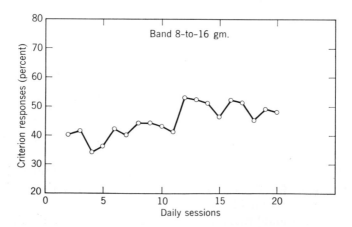

Figure 5-4 Mean per cent of total responses meeting the 8-to-16 gm. peak-force band criterion as a function of successive days for Group I.

sonable to view this behavioral phenomenon as a form of "self-imposed" variable ratio schedule in which the interaction of required effort, discriminative capacity, and perhaps amount of reinforcement comes to determine some point of stability.

Returning to the issue of the predictive value of the several theories that have been advanced to explain the increase in force of response during extinction, it may be well to review the specific positions each formulation might take with respect to the experiment here described.

Biological

To the extent that the several biological approaches ignore learning variables, it would seem that each would predict an increase in force during extinction but would not have anything to say about the relative ordering of Groups I, II, and III during extinction. This is undoubtedly an overconstraining view of, say, Amsel's conception, but it is difficult for us to apply his theory, predicated upon runway data, to the present bar-pressing situation.

Learning

Response Subclass. This learning approach, offered in detail by Schoenfeld and tested by Goldberg, would probably be most concerned with a comparison of the behavior of Groups I and II. Again, to the extent that other learning parameters can be ignored, it would seem that the Schoenfeld-Goldberg prediction would be that Group II (exposed during early acquisition to a 4-to-16-gm. band) should reflect during extinction the influence of its past reinforcement for lower response subclasses. Accordingly, Group II's force level during extinction should be lower than that of Group I.

As far as Group III is concerned, the "response-subclass-reinforcement" interpreters would probably predict that this group would emit force levels higher than either Group I or Group II. This behavior would be expected simply on the basis of the higher response subclasses that had been reinforced during acquisition.

Incidental Directional Reinforcement. Followers of this formulation, described by Notterman and Block, would predict—contrary to the response subclass theorists—that Group I should be lower during extinction than Group II. (The rationale for this view has been offered in the preceding pages.) From lowest to highest force level during extinction, the IDR theory would therefore expect the groups to order themselves I, II, III.

Examination of Fig. 5-2 indicates that this prediction is, indeed, borne out. A comparison of the change in mean peak force per animal between the last three days of conditioning and the three days of extinction for Group I with the change during the same time for Group II shows that the two groups differ at approximately the 0.05 level (by Wilcoxon's Unpaired Replicates, two-tailed test) and at the 0.025 level if the advantage of prior prediction is granted.

We trust it has been made amply clear to the reader that in no way do we consider this experiment to be a critical test for any theory. There is much that is sensible in the biological explanation of increased "vigor" during extinction. Similarly, the response-subclass formulation is reasonable as far as it goes. Our purpose in drawing attention to the incidental directional reinforcement theory is primarily to argue the importance of dynamic, as well as static, response properties. With this, we believe, all interested theorists can agree.

Chapter Six

Exteroceptive Cueing of Response Level: The Double-Band Discrimination

EXTENSION OF THE "BAND" discrimination situation is considered in this chapter.[1] Two separate "band" criteria, each with
an upper and lower peak-force limit for reinforcement, are used. The
momentarily "correct" band is correlated with an exteroceptive stimulus, light-on or light-off. In order for reinforcement to take place,
the peak force of response must fall within the prescribed limits indicated by the particular exteroceptive stimulus then present.

Skinner (1938, p. 338) described this sort of procedure as a "double discrimination." In the more usual discrimination training procedure, one stimulus is correlated with reinforcement (S^D), and the
other is not (S^Λ). Such training produces responding predominantly in
the presence of the stimulus correlated with reinforcement (S^D); a
situation of exactly this sort was examined in Chapter 4. During "double discrimination," reinforcement is always possible. Each stimulus
indicates the particular response variation that must occur in order
for reinforcement to take place.

The exteroceptive cueing of response level is implicit in many familiar examples of behavior. The size-weight illusion, for instance,
has been explained by the effect of the visually perceived size of the
object on the force of the motor response of lifting (Skinner, 1938;
Woodworth and Schlosberg, 1954). To produce a constant perceptible
change in the environment (that is, elevation of the physical object),
the force of the appropriate response must vary in proportion to the
weight of the object. When the density of two objects is apparently

[1] A preliminary report based on the data of this chapter was published by J. M.
Notterman and D. E. Mintz in *Science*, 1962, *135*, 1070–1071.

111

identical (no visually discriminable difference), discrepancy in size is likely to provide the exteroceptive stimulus basis for the different force emissions during the separate lifting responses. These force emissions themselves presumably affect the subsequent judgment. This behavior relates to the reinforcement history of the organism. Our physical environment provides a high positive correlation among many perceptible aspects of numerous stimulus complexes. The size as compared with the weight of objects, the force emitted as compared with the velocity imparted to objects, and the brightness as compared with the temperature of radiant sources are just a few of the many positively related characteristics that the behaving organism encounters in his typical environment.

The acquisition of behavior characterized by a relation between stimulus magnitude and response magnitude may be described as a form of closed-loop error detection and correction. Experimentally, the reinforcement may be the actual event of pellet delivery. In the nonexperimental environment the reinforcement may be in the maintenance or generation of some particular stimulus configuration. In driving an automobile, for instance, the momentary visually perceived configuration of the road and the position of the speedometer dial might be considered to provide the effective reinforcement for the behavior involved in positioning the steering wheel and depressing the accelerator pedal. The momentary magnitude of the stimulus (error or deviation) provides the cue for the magnitude of response. The response magnitude, in turn, produces a related change in the ensuing stimulus magnitude.

As noted in Chapter 4, the likelihood that the magnitude of the operant response and its discriminative stimulus are positively related produces a superficial similarity between the reflex dynamism for operant and that for respondent behavior. This situation, however, is fortuitous as to operant behavior. Depending on the reinforcement contingency, the organism may learn a positive or negative relation between the stimulus and response magnitudes. The preponderance of positive relations that exist in "natural" reinforcement contingencies relates to phenomena more appropriate to the science of physics than to the science of behavior.

In this study we chose two values of illumination to provide the cues for the appropriate level of force emission. In the single "band" experiment (Chapter 5) the exteroceptive cueing played a minor role, since the experimental environment and the reinforcement contingency were invariant. In the "double discrimination," the feedback

stimulus appropriate to a reinforced response is systematically correlated with the particular level of the exteroceptive stimulus (light-on
or light-off). Both stimuli must be present at specified and related
values. The relations may be described by the paradigms (see Chapter 4):

$$S_1{}^{De} \longrightarrow R_1 \longrightarrow S_1{}^{Di} \longrightarrow S^R \qquad (1)$$

$$S_2{}^{De} \longrightarrow R_2 \longrightarrow S_2{}^{ni} \longrightarrow S^R \qquad (2)$$

In each instance the exteroceptive stimulus present indicates the
proprioceptive and cutaneous feedback that must also be present in
order for reinforcement to take place. Generation of the appropriate
feedback stimulus in turn requires emission of the particular response
called for by the "differentiation" contingency.

The primary distinction between this procedure and a "choice" procedure such as might occur in maze learning or "matching to sample" (Skinner, 1950; Blough, 1959) is that R_1 and R_2 and their associated feedback belong to a single continuum. Unlike responses identified as "turning right" -"turning left" or "S^D key"—"S^Δ key," different peak forces of response bear a quantitative rather than topographical relation. Additionally, during the emission of a correct
"choice" response, exteroceptive as well as proprioceptive changes are
generally involved. In the foregoing paradigms, R_1 and R_2 are dis-
tinguishable only on a proprioceptive or cutaneous basis.

We are assuming that the generation of a particular force of response generates unique sensory events (feedback) and that these are
essential to the process of response differentiation. We are not con-
tending that the behavioral processes in a "double discrimination"
based on the peak force of lever pressing differ from those of choice
point learning in a maze. Rather, the distinction rests on the quantitative and proprioceptive role of feedback in "double discrimination" and its qualitative and exteroceptive function in choice point
learning. At least at the present level of experimental sophistication
this distinction seems genuine.

In the "double discrimination" here described, two separate discriminative capacities may be involved. One is the visual discrimination of the exteroceptive light; the other, the proprioceptive discrim-

ination of the force level. For the exteroceptive stimuli we have chosen two levels of illumination shown by past experimental experience to have very little cross-generalization in the well-trained subject. The distribution of peak force of response is taken as a measure of generalization in the case of force discrimination.

Method

Eight subjects were used. Each subject performed under two peak-force "band" criteria. The momentarily correct band was correlated with light-on (20 foot-candles at the cage floor) or light-off. The two peak-force bands were 5 to 10 gm. and 15 to 20 gm. For half of the subjects (31, 32, 33, and 34) light-on was correlated with the high band; for the other subjects (35, 36, 39, and 25) light-on was correlated with the low band.

Daily sessions lasted 20 minutes and 40 seconds for each subject. Each of the two bands (and its correlated exteroceptive stimulus) was in effect for half of this total time. The sequence of the two conditions followed the same temporal program described in Chapter 4. Every response meeting the appropriate criterion was reinforced with a 45-mg. food pellet. Consequently, the number of pellets any animal received on a particular day depended on his performance, but the training time for all subjects was constant. Initial training was carried out for 41 days.

Four of the animals were run in a second phase of the experiment. Ten days of additional training, similar to the initial training, were given, followed by two days during which the reinforcement criteria operated as before, but the exteroceptive cue was continuously in the light-off condition. Animals 31, 32, 25, and 36 were used in this phase; thus, for two animals the low band was cued and for two the high band was cued.

Results and Discussion

In examining the data, we have considered separately the performance in the high-band and low-band condition for each animal. One major purpose of the study was a demonstration of the acquisition of the "double-discrimination" behavior.

In Fig. 6-1 the daily percentages of total responses meeting the band

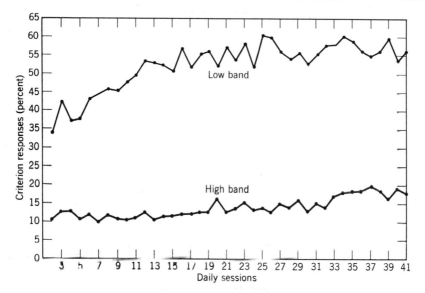

Figure 6-1 Group mean per cent of total responses meeting the low-band (5-to-10 gm.) and high-band (15-to-20 gm.) reinforcement criteria as a function of successive days of training.

criteria are shown, averaged for all eight animals. The performance on day 1 of acquisition is omitted since certain procedural irregularities were required to maintain responding for some animals. This generally involved a few reinforcements for noncriterion responses.

In both the high- and low-band performance there is a progressive increase in the percentage of responses meeting criterion. The increase appears to continue even beyond the first 30 days of training. The thirty-day period represents more than 10 hours of exposure to the schedule contingencies and between 3,000 and 6,000 reinforcements for each animal. No systematic changes in the rate of response were observed for the group as a whole beyond the first few days of training, when a general increase was evident.

Days 39, 40, and 41 were taken as representative of a final and stable mode of performance and are examined in detail. Table 6-1 contains several measures of performance for the eight subjects. For each subject in the high-band schedule, mean peak force is higher and the percentage of responses meeting the criterion is lower than for the low band. The high- and low-band rates of response (including non-criterion responses) are more subject to individual differences. Some

TABLE 6-1

Measures of Performance under Low- and High-Band Conditions

Subjects	Mean Peak Force (gm.)		Criterion Responses (per cent)		Mean Response Rate (responses/min.)	
	Low Band	High Band	Low Band	High Band	Low Band	High Band
High Band Light-on						
31	5.6	11.2	60.8	9.5	26.0	12.1
32	6.7	12.4	65.3	26.2	24.3	29.1
33	8.2	13.9	34.5	18.8	21.9	21.6
34	7.7	13.2	58.0	29.3	16.7	17.5
Low Band Light-on						
35	7.4	12.0	50.7	17.0	22.7	25.6
36	6.7	10.9	77.7	6.6	20.1	4.5
39	8.4	14.0	50.8	20.1	25.2	19.8
25	5.6	11.3	52.1	11.5	26.4	16.3

measure of control, however, appears to be exerted by the relative frequency of reinforcement.

In order to examine the relation between relative frequency of reinforcement and relative response rate the following analysis was performed: for each animal the ratio of response rate in the low and high band was computed, and a similar computation was performed for the rate of reinforcement in each band. The rank order correlation of these two measures for the group was .79. In other words, the animals with the widest relative discrepancy in the rate of reinforcement in the two bands also showed the widest relative discrepancy in the frequency of response and vice versa. Of itself this observation is not surprising. However, the data show an interestingly high measure of conformity to a linear relation when plotted on log-log coordinates. This plot is shown in Fig. 6-2.

The straight line plotted in Fig. 6-2 represents the least-squares solution for best fit. At first blush one might expect a unit intercept, that is, response rates would be equal when the reinforcement rates are equal. However, the empirical equation is $y = .66x^{.473}$ (or approximately $y = \frac{2\sqrt{x}}{3}$), predicting a ratio of .66 between the rates of response when the rates of reinforcement in the two bands are equal. We must recall that the schedules produce responses in the two bands that differ in their physical properties. For the group, the ratio of mean peak force in the low band compared with the high band is .57. Although it may be mere coincidence, this value is quite close to the ratio of .66 predicted for the relative rates of response.

If the suggestions of this analysis are correct, the double-discrimination schedule would appear to produce an interaction between the two bands. In Chapter 3 we provided data indicating that the rate of response was unaffected by the reinforcement criterion. However, those data relate to performance with a single regularly reinforced criterion for a given animal. The successively presented stimuli in the "double discrimination" might well acquire cueing properties for re-

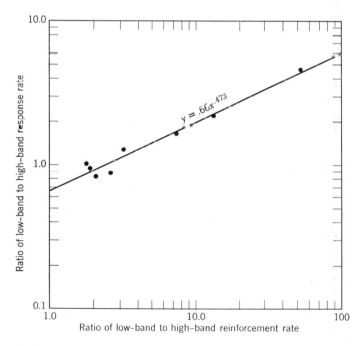

Figure 6-2 Scattergram of ratio of low-band to high-band response rate and ratio of low-band to high-band reinforcement rate. Each point represents an individual animal; the plotted line indicates the "least squares" best fit.

sponse rate as well as response peak force. Schedule interactions of the sort are not uncommon (Reynolds, 1961a, 1961b).

The implication of this analysis is that the rate of reinforcement, the force (or effortfulness) of response, and the response rate are interrelated. A power function appears to describe these data fairly well. That a power function may describe the relation between the rates of reinforcement and response has been noted previously by Catania (1963).

The distributions of peak force of response for four subjects are shown in Figs. 6-3 and 6-4. For each animal, combined distributions for days 2, 3, and 4 and for days 39, 40, and 41 are plotted. During the early stages of acquisition there was little difference between the high- and low-band performance. At the end of training, well-differentiated distributions are evident for subjects 32, 34, and 35. All of the subjects show a tendency for the distributions to peak within the low band, while the peaking for the high band falls somewhat below the band limits. This same characteristic may be noted in the means of the distributions in Table 6-1. Subject 36 (Fig. 6-3) shows a high-band distribution that does not reflect the typical displacement away from the low-band distribution along the peak-force continuum. In Table 6-1 it was shown that this animal maintained a very low rate of response and a low frequency of reinforcement in the high-band condition. The distribution for this animal suggests that the high-band reinforcement failed to exert sufficient control over the peak force of response. Although occasional high-band reinforcements did occur, it appears that the high band was effectively an S^{Δ} condition for animal 36. It may also be more than coincidence that this animal had the highest percentage of criterion responses in the low band.

Among the eight animals there was no apparent difference in the performance related to the particular light intensity that was correlated with the force level. Observed high or low forces seemed to depend only on the reinforcement contingency.

An additional measure of the effect of the light as a controlling stimulus was made by examining the first response after each stimulus change. If the light were exerting no control, an increase or decrease in the peak force of response would be equally likely. (This assumption was validated by determining that there was no significant over-all tendency for forces to go either up or down more frequently.) Based on a sign test, the entire group shows a significant (5% level) increase in peak force for the first response in the presence of each

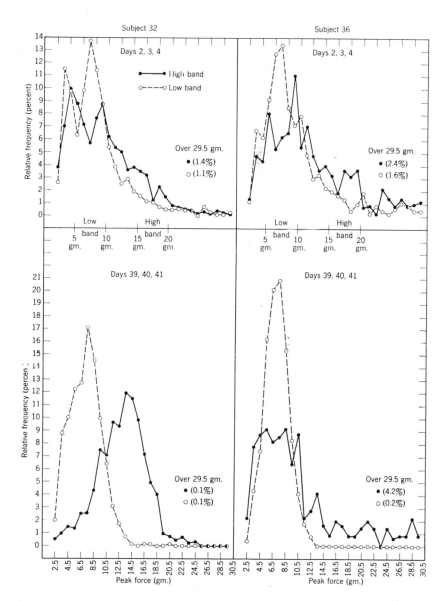

Figure 6-3 Relative frequency distributions of peak force of response for subjects 32 and 36 during the early and final stages of training of double discrimination. The low (5-to-10 gm.) and high (15-to-20 gm.) reinforcement bands are indicated.

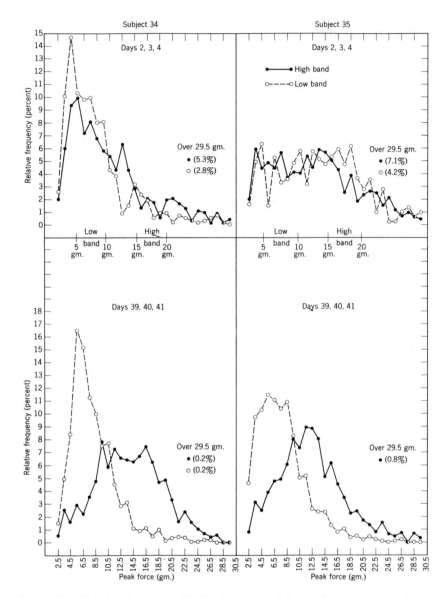

Figure 6-4   Relative frequency distributions of peak force of response for subjects 34 and 35 during the early and final stages of training of double discrimination. The low (5-to-10 gm.) and high (15-to-20 gm.) reinforcement bands are indicated.

high-band stimulus and a significant decrease for the first response following each change to the low-band stimulus.[2]

It is appropriate to consider the first response after the stimulus change because the new reinforcement contingency in effect has not yet had an opportunity to operate. As will be shown later, the occurrence of a reinforced response itself appears to exert considerable control over subsequent responses. Since a daily session involved only 19 stimulus changes, the preponderance of responses occurred in a context of the same reinforcement contingency for immediately antecedent behavior. Only for the first response after the stimulus change will repetition of a reinforced response fail to meet the criterion. Consequently, antecedent reinforced behavior *cannot* provide the discriminative basis for the subsequent level of force emission for those first responses following a stimulus change.

It is not likely that the higher forces during high-band performance simply reflect a force elevation attributable to less frequent reinforcement. As was shown in Chapter 4, S^Δ, with no reinforcement, produces higher peak forces of response than does S^D. Nevertheless, these higher forces in extinction are characterized by a skewing rather than a displacement of the distribution. This peak-force-distribution skewing is a general feature of behavior whenever extinction occurs.

In addition to the peaking of the distribution for the high band, the general increase in the relative frequency of reinforcement for high-band performance over the course of training (see Fig. 6-1) suggests an effective differentiation related to the reinforcement of high-band responses. Along with peak force, the mean duration of response is greater for the high-band than for the low-band distributions. These values are shown in Table 6-2. The group means differ significantly (Wilcoxon Paired Replicates, 5% level). This finding is similar to others we have reported in which the gross effects found for the peak force also occur for the duration of response.

Exteroceptive Discriminative Control

The two exteroceptive stimulus conditions (light-on and light-off) were made available to the subjects to provide a discriminative basis for the appropriate band performance. The differentiated distributions of peak force suggest that the stimulus control was actually

---

[2] It is interesting to note that there also appeared to be an unconditioned effect related to stimulus change. At the beginning of acquisition there was a significant *decrease* in the force of the first response following *either* stimulus change.

TABLE 6-2

Mean Response Duration
(seconds)

Subjects	Low Band	High Band
31	0.26	0.37
32	0.26	0.29
33	0.30	0.39
34	0.45	0.56
35	0.27	0.34
36	0.37	0.61
39	0.27	0.20
25	0.42	0.67
$\overline{X}$	0.33	0.43

acquired. A significant change in the peak force of response in the appropriate direction for the first response after each stimulus change was found (p. 118). Nevertheless, the final phase of the experiment provides evidence to indicate that a relatively good level of performance may be maintained without an exteroceptive discriminative stimulus.

During the last two days of the final phase of the experiment, four of the animals performed in the presence of an exteroceptive cue that did not change during the session, although the usual program of band-criterion alternation was carried out. An index of the effect of this procedure is shown in Table 6-3. The tabulated ratios indicate the proportion of responses meeting criterion following the elimination of a varying exteroceptive cue as compared with those that met criterion before the elimination of the cue. The indices lower than 1.00 for three of the animals show a reduction in the relative frequency of responses meeting the criterion when the effective band

TABLE 6-3

Ratio of Criterion Responses Following S^{De} Removal
(per cent after : per cent before)

	31	32	36	25
Low Band	0.90	0.69	1.00	0.95
High Band	0.71	0.89	1.03	0.70

is no longer systematically cued. For animal 36 there appears to be no essential difference. It is interesting to recall that the other data for this subject suggest a single-band mode of performance. The failure of the change in conditions to disrupt its performance is consistent with this suggestion.

The distributions of peak force of response for two subjects immediately before and after S^{D_e} removal are shown in Fig. 6-5. Both subjects show some decrease in the relative frequency of criterion responses for both bands. However, the distributions still indicate conformity to the criteria after the exteroceptive cue has been removed.

The basis for maintaining a distinction between the high- and low-band distributions of peak force of response in the absence of a systematically correlated exteroceptive cue requires explanation. An illustration of a subject (animal 32) that maintained a well-differentiated distribution of peak force under this condition is shown in Fig. 6-6-1. For this subject, both high- and low-band distributions reflect the reinforcement contingency, despite the absence of the appropriate exteroceptive cue.

An explanation for maintaining the differentiation may be sought in the interaction between the differentiated behavior and its immediate behavioral antecedents. In other words, some measure of discriminative control of behavior rests with behavior immediately preceding it—without implying an unequivocal tendency toward repetition of reinforced behavior. Repetition will be likely only if repetition itself has been previously reinforced. For instance, it is demonstrated in Chapter 9 that despite reinforcement of very high-force responses, certain modified fixed-ratio schedules invariably have low peak-force responses following reinforced responses of high force. The force decline appears to relate to the experimental contingencies that produce reinforcement upon the occurrence of such a pattern.

In the present "double-discrimination" procedure, there was—for any response—a high probability that the subsequent response would occur with the same reinforcement contingency in effect. Consequently, repetition of a reinforced response would be likely to lead to reinforcement.

Discriminative control might be expected to be acquired by the reinforced behavior plus the reinforcement. In terms of a paradigm:

$$\left[R_1{}^D \longrightarrow S_1{}^{D_i} \longrightarrow S^R \right] \longrightarrow R_1{}^D \dots \tag{3}$$

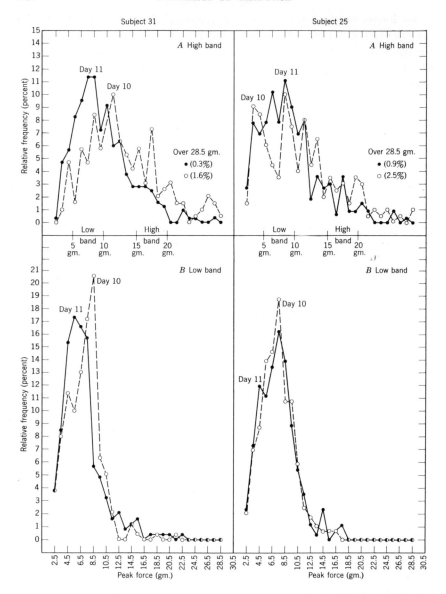

Figure 6-5   Relative frequency distributions of peak force of response for subjects 31 and 25 for: (*A*) the high (15-to-20 gm.) and (*B*) the low (5-to-10 gm.) band reinforcement criteria. The distributions for last day for which an exteroceptive stimulus was present (day 10) and the subsequent day (day 11) for which this stimulus was not provided are both shown.

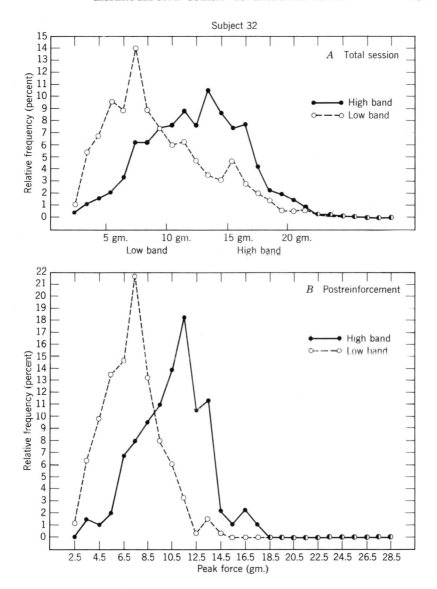

Figure 6-6 Relative frequency distributions of peak force of response for subject 32 during double-discrimination training subsequent to the elimination of the exteroceptive stimulus. In (A) the distributions for the entire session are shown; (B) contains the distributions only of those responses that were preceded by a reinforced response falling within the appropriate band.

When the reinforcement is absent, the condition for a switch may
be established. This is represented:

$$\left[\begin{array}{c} \overset{\downarrow\;\rule{2cm}{0.4pt}}{R_1{}^D \longrightarrow S_1{}^{D_i} \;\; \longrightarrow\!\!\!/\!\!\!\longrightarrow\; S^R} \end{array} \right] \longrightarrow R_2{}^D \;\ldots \qquad (4)$$

In order to examine the relation suggested in paradigm 3, the frequency distributions of peak force of response for animal 32 were
computed for only the first response after each reinforced response
(on the two days when the exteroceptive stimulus was kept constant).
These distributions are shown in Fig. 6-6-B. They represent a subclass
of the distributions for the entire session, which are shown in Fig.
6-6-A.

It is apparent that the distribution of responses following high-
band reinforcement is markedly differentiated from the distribution
of responses following low-band reinforcement. Further, these postreinforcement distributions are characterized by low variability (significantly different from the parent distributions at the 5% level, F
ratio, two-tailed test). Interestingly, the high-band distribution shows
a considerable downward shift from the force levels of the criterion
band. Only 4.4 per cent of the responses following high-band reinforcement fall within the band; none exceed the 20-gm. upper limit
of the band. This is descriptive of the general tendency (noted earlier
in this discussion) for high-band performance to peak below the band.
With regard to the low band, 68.7 per cent of the post-reinforced responses constituted repetition of the criterion range (5 to 10 gm.).

The sequential patterning of response is further evident from the
data in Table 6-4. Each tabulated value indicates the conditional

TABLE 6-4

Per Cent of Responses Meeting Criterion

Number of Successive Unreinforced Responses	Subjects			
	31	32	36	25
0	63.4	68.7	81.6	70.5
1	62.0	58.0	70.8	64.0
2	54.3	17.7	50.0	38.7

probability of the animals' emission of a criterion response following sequences of various numbers of unreinforced responses. The data are shown for the low band only. The row designated "zero" (0) unreinforced responses indicates the proportion of occasions when the first response following a reinforced response was also reinforced. If the probability of meeting the criterion were independent of the behavior preceding each response, each subject would be expected to produce the same conditional probability of criterion response, regardless of the number of antecedent unreinforced responses. The regular decrease in the percentages indicates that emission of a criterion response is most likely immediately following a reinforced response. Nonreinforcement leads to a progressive decrease in the probability that an individual response will meet the criterion. Consequently, noncriterion responses tend to cluster in extended sequence. For the present, it must remain a matter of conjecture as to whether it is the passage of time or the events that occur during the time that affect the subsequent behavior. It is noteworthy that the behavior following a string of unreinforced responses appears to have the characteristics of extinction responding—elevated force and increased variability.

As to the high band, the small sample size produced less reliable measures, but it should be mentioned that all four animals showed the greatest probability of reaching criterion after several unreinforced responses rather than immediately after reinforcement. However, this observation is in accord with the negative force displacement following high band reinforcement shown for subject 32 in Fig. 6-6 and previously noted as characteristic of the group.

Some Aspects of Force Differentiation

We have assumed that the emission of force in the lever-press situation generates related sensory events (feedback). The band-reinforcement contingency establishes a condition in which only certain variations of the feedback are systematically related to reinforcement. By inference, the distribution of the peak force of response during performance describes a related distribution of feedback stimuli.

In this situation, as with the psychophysical method of adjustments, the subject modifies his environment until it conforms to some experimentally specified condition. In psychophysics the subject is instructed or has learned to adjust the exteroceptive stimulus responsive to his behavior until the stimulus is judged "not different" from some standard. In band discrimination, the animal adjusts its force until it is "not different" from the "standard" that has been established by its reinforcement history. The primary distinction is that in the psychophysical experiment the subject is modifying a stimulus that is directly available to the experimenter as well as to the subject.

In examining the double-band data certain similarities to generalization data are noteworthy. For every subject the variability of high-band performance is significantly greater than for low-band performance (F ratio, two-tailed test, 5% level). This is consistent with a monotonic relation between stimulus magnitude and the size of the j.n.d. (just noticeable difference). In addition, a relation comparable with the Weber ratio is suggested. Taking the ratio of the standard deviation of the distributions to the midpoints of the band, we have an expression of the familiar form $\Delta S/S$. For the group average, this value is 0.423 for the high band, and 0.488 for the low band (the band midpoints of 17.5- and 7.5-gm. peak force were used).

It is also interesting to note that the force distributions tended to peak below the band midpoints. For the low band (5-to-10-gm.) this negative displacement was very slight and the modal frequency fell within the band limits. In the high band (15-to-20-gm.) the displacement of the distributions away from the band actually produced modal frequencies below the reinforced range. This feature of the behavior may reflect a tendency toward less effortful performance. On the other hand, and again drawing on the psychophysical analogy, the displacement may be a form of negative time error such as is found in weight-lifting comparisons (Woodworth and Schlosberg, 1954, Chapter 8).

In dealing with the double-band discrimination, the effects of band width, band locus, and the arbitrary relations between stimulus and response that are reinforced are fairly apparent. Although sensory and effector capacities are involved, the salient features of the performance are controlled by the reinforcement history. It is likely that many behavioral situations involving the relation between a behavioral continuum and a stimulus continuum are subject to considerable influence by a reinforcement regimen. The dynamic relation between stimulus and response magnitude undoubtedly depends in a large measure on just what particular relation the organism has learned.

Conclusions

In the exteroceptive cueing of response peak force, several variables appear to exert direct control over the behavior. The exteroceptive discriminative stimulus itself effectively sets the occasion for a particular level of force emission. The dynamic relation between stimulus and response magnitude depends on the reinforcement contingency. This relation may be inverse or direct.

In addition to the discriminative function of an experimentally provided stimulus, the organism's own reinforced behavior appears to exert discriminative control. This phenomenon is implicit in the general tendency toward stereotyped responding that occurs when behavior is regularly reinforced at some invariant reinforcement criterion. In the "double discrimination" it was found that responses immediately following reinforcement tended to produce distributions with low variability. The high-band postreinforcement distributions were well differentiated from the low-band postreinforcement distributions. The occurrence of a reinforced response appeared to function as a discriminative stimulus for the subsequent response. It is suggested that this tendency toward repetition developed because the experimental conditions produced a high probability that repetition of reinforced behavior would lead to reinforcement. When the exteroceptive discriminative stimulus was no longer correlated with the reinforcement criterion, the relative frequency of criterion responses decreased. It was shown that for the low band condition the likelihood of meeting the criterion was greatest immediately following reinforcement.

For both high- and low-band performance there was a tendency for the peak-force distributions to peak somewhat below the midpoint of the reinforcement range. For the high band this negative displacement of the distributions was sufficient to bring the modal performance below the reinforced range. In general, high-band performance produced less frequent reinforcement and greater response variability than did the low band.

In rate of response, individual differences among the animals produced diverse results. Although every animal received more frequent reinforcement for the low-band condition, some animals responded more frequently under the high-band condition. Those animals showing the lowest relative frequency of reinforcement for the high band also showed very low rates of response in this condition. The effect in this case is suggestive of S^Δ performance under traditional discrimination procedures.

An analysis of the performance during "double discrimination" may be made in terms of the role of behavior-produced stimulation or "feedback." It is suggested that certain effector events within the response are themselves cued by antecedent response-produced sensory events. These patterns conform to the general principles of discriminative behavior and strengthen the view (see Chapter 4) that the phenomenon of response differentiation is a special case of stimulus discrimination.

Chapter Seven

Feedback

SOME CONCEPT OF FEEDBACK appears essential to an analysis of the force characteristics of operant behavior. When an organism behaves, it modifies its environment. The resulting changes may in turn provide the effective cues for subsequent behavior. Response chaining and speech disruption with delayed feedback are just two among many phenomena that illustrate the cue producing function the response itself may perform.

The several studies discussed in this chapter are intended to demonstrate that the force of a response depends upon continuous sensory information generated by the emission of the force itself. This feedback is probably a composite of both cutaneous responses and pro prioceptive muscle sensations. We are proposing that a distribution of the response property, peak force, implies a distribution of the related feedback stimuli.

The process involved in the emission of a precise peak force of response would seem analogous to the psychophysical method of adjustments. For instance, in the emission of a force band response, the animal may apply increasing force to the lever until it has produced those feedback conditions that have previously been correlated with reinforcement. The completion of an "adjustment" is indicated by response termination. The variations in peak force in such a situation may in part reflect a process essentially identical to stimulus generalization.

Proprioceptive and cutaneous feedback must for the present remain dependent variables. Nevertheless, the two experimental procedures reported in this chapter contribute fairly strongly to the argument that the force characteristics of response *can* be modified through the

131

direct or indirect manipulation of feedback and that interference with cutaneous feedback *can* disrupt this performance. For the manipulation of feedback, we have employed exteroceptive cues that appear during the response only when a specified force is emitted. For feedback disruption we administered procaine hydrochloride to the rat's paw, producing an essential deafferentation.

Exteroceptive Feedback

In conventional operant-conditioning studies using the basic Skinnerian procedure, the subject is provided with an exteroceptive correlate of force at the threshold level. The audible click of the microswitch provides this auditory feedback. Also, in the usual procedure, microswitch closure indicates that the force criterion for reinforcement as well as the response threshold have been achieved. Consequently, the subject is furnished with a discriminative stimulus on each occasion when its force has just reached the minimum level required for reinforcement.

At this juncture it is important to recall that the operation of our manipulandum produces no sounds and involves essentially no displacement. In the present chapter, we seek to demonstrate that when cues are provided to indicate attainment of the reinforcement criterion, the subject's behavior is appropriately modified. When microswitch manipulanda are used, it is likely that the sound of the switch itself does much to contribute to the physical properties of the responses that are generated. The systematic stimuli given the subjects when they have emitted responses meeting the reinforcement criterion have been a coincidental, though perhaps useful, aspect of instrumentation of traditional operant procedures.

Exteroceptive Feedback in Band Reinforcement

With a band criterion the subject emits forces that vary over a period of time, but only upon completion of the response is it provided with any exteroceptive stimulus indicating that the peak force fell within the band. This, of course, is the reinforcer itself. We have assumed that when a subject learns to emit responses meeting the criterion, proprioceptive and cutaneous feedback plays an essential role in the process. The first two studies considered in this chapter are based on the assumption that exteroceptive feedback differs in function from this internal feedback only in terms of its origin. The feedback provided was in the form of auditory and visual cues that were initiated by meeting the criterion. The procedure may be described by the paradigm:

$$S^D \longrightarrow R \longrightarrow S^{D_i} + S^{D_e} \longrightarrow S^R$$

Both internal (S^{D_i}) and exteroceptive (S^{D_e}) feedback loops are shown.

Band Reinforcement Feedback Procedure

The 12 subjects comprising Groups I and II used in the peak-force band experiment (Chapter 5) were subsequently used in the feedback condition. To restate the earlier training briefly, Group I had 20 days of CRF, with 50 reinforcements per day for responses meeting the 8-to-16-gm. peak-force band criterion. Group II performed with a 4-to-16-gm. band for the first seven of the 20 days and was then switched to the 8-to-16-gm. band. Subsequently, three daily 10-minute extinction sessions were run for both groups.

After extinction, all subjects were given six days of reconditioning with the 8-to-16-gm. band. Feedback was introduced following the reconditioning. The feedback stimuli were an overhead light providing approximately 20 foot-candles of illumination at the cage floor and a code oscillator sounding at 1000 cycles per second, approximately 30 decibels sound pressure level. The onset and cessation of the two stimuli were simultaneous. The onset occurred as soon as the response-force level reached the lower limit of the band. Both stimuli continued to operate until either the force level exceeded the upper limit of the band or the force level fell below the response threshold (2.5 gm.), that is, the response ended. When a response ended, the reinforcement was delivered at approximately the same moment the stimuli stopped. During responses in which the force exceeded the upper limit of the band (precluding reinforcement), a return to a force level within the band did not reinstate the stimuli.

Six days of training were conducted with the exteroceptive feedback related to the 8-to-16-gm. reinforcement band. A seventh session was run during which the exteroceptive feedback was withheld.

After training with the 8-to-16-gm. band, all animals were run for 16 days on a 10-to-14-gm. band (close-in phase). In the close-in phase, only one half of the animals received exteroceptive feedback. The two groups were established on a basis of pairs, selected with regard to previous experimental experience, the members of each pair assigned to the new groups at random.

Feedback Effects in the 8-to-16-gm. Reinforcement Band

Despite the introduction of feedback, no systematic changes in performance were noted during the six days of such training. A slight increase in the proportion of responses falling within the band and a slight decrease in the proportion below the band were observed, but considerable variation from animal to animal rendered this effect unreliable. Since all of the animals had previously been trained extensively with the 8-to-16-gm. peak-force reinforcement criterion, it is quite likely that a performance limit had been reached. The addition of auditory and visual cues, indicating the force level was within the band, apparently did not provide a usable supplement to the behavior established with proprioceptive and cutaneous feedback.

As a next procedural step, we sought to examine whether the behavior might be altered when the exteroceptive feedback was removed. A comparison of the group performance on the sixth day of exteroceptive feedback training and the next day when the feedback was eliminated is shown in Fig. 7-1. The frequency distribution of response peak force shows a significant shift in the direction of greater force (Kolmogorov-Smirnov, 5% level).

Eleven of the 12 animals displayed the tendency shown for the group in Fig. 7-1. On this count it is important to note that both above-band and within-band responses produced the auditory and visual feedback. Above-band responses led to a termination of these stimuli at the moment the force exceeded the upper limit of the band. However, these feedback stimuli should provide a readily discriminable difference between responses peaking below and above the 8-gm. lower limit of the band.

Responses that did not produce the auditory and visual stimuli during feedback training were never reinforced. The animal's failure to produce these cues became a condition requiring greater force. On the day when the exteroceptive stimuli were withheld, the tendency to increase force to the level formerly required for the introduction of exteroceptive feedback apparently led to the observed force increase. The exteroceptive cues now indicated that all responses were "below

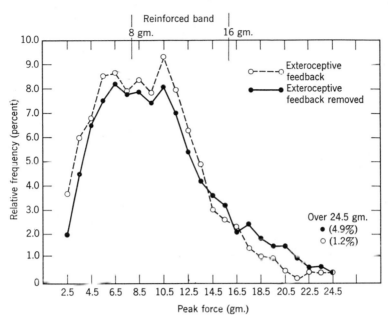

Figure 7-1   Relative frequency distributions of peak force of response on the last day of band reinforcement (8-to-16 gm. peak force) with exteroceptive feedback and the subsequent day with feedback removed. The curves reflect the combined distributions of 12 subjects.

band." Since within-band responses were still reinforced, the animals were provided with what were essentially conflicting cues, that is, feedback from their own behavior still maintained a systematic discriminative relation to reinforcement, although the relation between exteroceptive feedback and reinforcement was abolished.

Feedback effects were observed only after the feedback was removed. This interesting aspect of the experiment suggests that even cues added to behavior that has already been stabilized may come to exert control over that behavior. The control, however, need not be observed as a change in performance. When some performance limit has already been reached, there appears to be what might be called a shift in reliance. The newly introduced stimuli come to share some of the control vested in the stimuli that were formerly available. This argument suggests that the effects of introducing feedback may be more notable during acquisition. The next phase of the experiment was directed at an examination of this hypothesis.

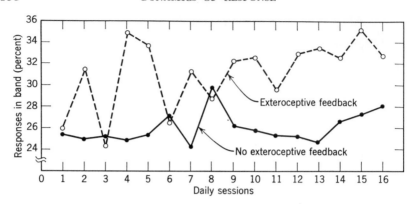

Figure 7-2 Per cent of total responses falling within the 10-to-14 gm. peak-force reinforcement band as a function of successive days of training. Data reflect the performance of two groups of subjects, one receiving, the other not receiving exteroceptive feedback.

Feedback during a Band Close-In

In this phase of the experiment the band was reduced from 8-to-16-gm. to 10-to-14-gm. peak force. The visual and auditory feedback stimuli were systematically provided for only six of the 12 animals. The mean percentage of responses meeting this new criterion is plotted for the "with" and the "without" feedback groups in Fig. 7-2. Although there are fluctuations in the early stages of this training, during the final stages the "with" feedback group is consistently meeting the criterion a greater proportion of the time.

The nature of the distinction between the performances of the two groups is more readily apparent in Fig. 7-3. This figure shows the averaged relative frequency distributions of peak force of response for the two groups. These data indicate that the availability of exteroceptive feedback tends to generate responses of sufficient force to produce the feedback.

Feedback in a Double Discrimination

A second study examining the effect of the introduction of exteroceptive feedback was conducted as an extension of the experimental regimen for four of the subjects in the double discrimination procedure (Chapter 6). These subjects, it will be remembered, performed

in a high band (15 to 20 gm.) and a low band (5 to 10 gm.), each cued
by a different light brightness. The four animals used in the present
study included two from the light-on low-band group and two from
the light-on high-band group.

The feedback procedure was similar to the one just described. When
a response reached the force level of the lower limit of the momentarily
correct band, the oscillator sounded (the feedback light was not used
since a light was already serving a discriminative function). It continued to sound until either the force exceeded the upper limit of
the band or the force fell below threshold. Ten days of such training
were carried out. Except for the exteroceptive feedback, the procedure
was a continuation of the first 41 days of training (see Chapter 6).

In Fig. 7-4, the relative frequency distributions of peak force of
response for the first and last (tenth) days of feedback training are
shown. It is apparent that with the extended training there is a shift
toward the force values that produce the oscillator tone. It can be

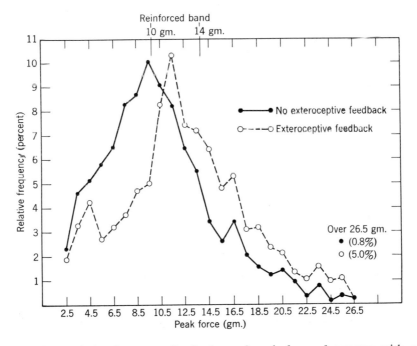

Figure 7-3   Relative frequency distributions of peak force of response with a
10-to-14 gm. peak-force reinforcement criterion. The curves represent the performance of the final day shown in Fig. 7-2.

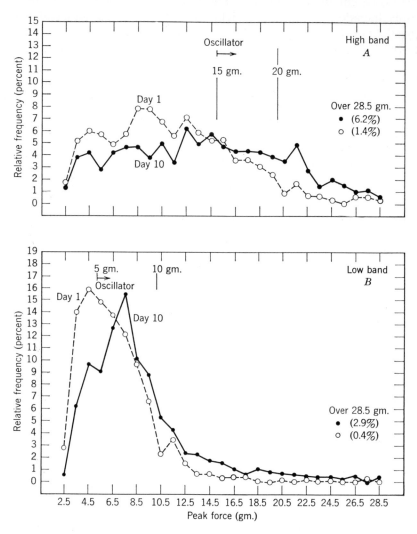

Figure 7-4 Relative frequency distributions of peak force of response during "double-discrimination" training with exteroceptive feedback. Curves represent the first and tenth days' performances with the 15-to-20 gm. peak-force reinforcement criterion (*A*) and with the 5-to-10 gm. criterion (*B*).

noted that the consistent effect is a reduction in the frequency of be-low-band responses for both the high and the low bands.

The progressive changes in the relative frequency of below-band responses may be seen in Fig. 7-5. For comparison purposes, the data for the last three days of the initial conditioning are included. Para-doxically, the initial effect of the introduction of the auditory feed-back is an increase in the frequency of below-band responses. These, of course, are responses below the level that produces the sounding of the oscillator. It is possible that this immediate (and presumably unconditioned) effect reflects aversive properties of the oscillator, that

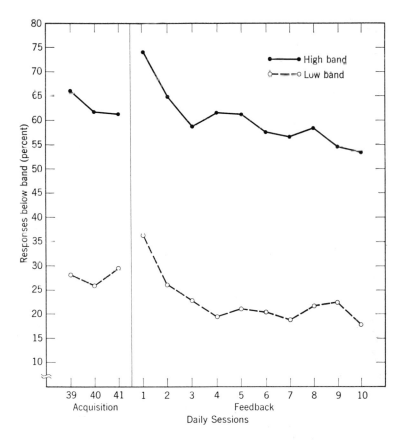

Figure 7-5   Per cent of total responses falling below the high (15-to-20 gm.) and low (5-to-10 gm.) reinforcement-criterion bands as a function of successive days. For comparison, the final three days of initial training without feedback are shown immediately preceding the ten days of training with exteroceptive feedback.

is, a mild punishment and consequent depression of high-force responses. The phenomenon is also reminiscent of the force decline that was noted whenever there was a stimulus change during the early training in double discrimination (Chapter 6, p. 121).

Whatever the basis for the initial force decline (increase in below-band frequency), the frequency of below-band responses decreases with

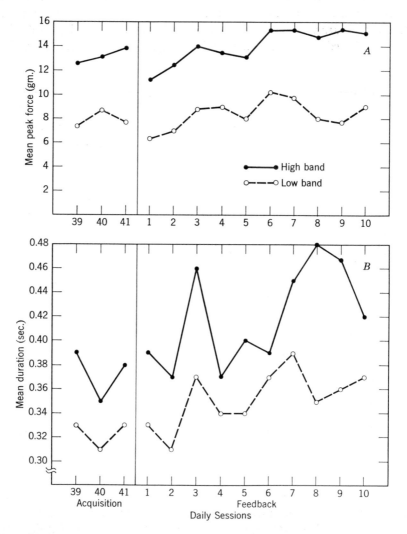

Figure 7-6 Mean peak force (*A*) and mean duration of response (*B*) as a function of successive days. Curves represent the same performance shown in Fig. 7-5.

progressive training. At the end of ten days, these frequencies are sub-stantially below those characteristic of initial acquisition. The animals have learned to emit a greater proportion of responses that reach at least the minimum force level required to produce the auditory feed-back.

The mean peak force and mean duration of response for the four subjects are shown in Fig. 7-6. Although the changes in the two re-sponse properties tended to be parallel, introduction of feedback did not diminish response duration on the first day, but did reduce mean peak force, possibly because the oscillator onset was systematically related to specific force magnitudes and not contingent upon particular response duration variants.

It is noteworthy that after several days of exteroceptive feedback, the mean peak force was in the vicinity of the lower limit of the high band. It should be recalled that the mean peak force was consistently below the lower limit of this band when feedback was not employed (Chapter 6).

General Effects of Exteroceptive Feedback

Both of the studies in which exteroceptive stimuli were system-atically related to within-band responses show comparable results. In general, there is a tendency for the peak-force distributions to shift in the direction of producing the feedback, necessitating an increase in the level of force emission. Since this force increase also produces a greater relative frequency of reinforcement, the extero-ceptive feedback maintains its control. A limit to this kind of control would appear to exist only when a force increase simply shifts non-reinforced responses from the below-band to the above-band category, as might happen with a very narrow band. Implicit in this argument is the notion that onset of feedback tends to establish a cue for the termination of force emission.

It seems certain that the changes in behavior here described reflect the acquisition of a discrimination. The subject is never reinforced when it fails to produce the exteroceptive feedback; it is frequently reinforced when it does. It is in this sense that the onset of the extero-ceptive stimulus may be considered as a cue for "response termina-tion." Viewed in this manner, the analysis of a single response (force as a function of time) is comparable with the analysis of a sequence of chained responses (Keller and Schoenfeld, 1950). Both analyses show that the stimuli generated by the behavior at any moment provide the cueing for subsequent behavior and possibly the reinforcement for antecedent behavior.

The way we have used exteroceptive feedback introduces certain difficulties. Two classes of response produce the feedback: within-band responses and above-band responses. The animal must again rely on cues from its own behavior to discriminate between these two classes. When the stimuli terminate and its force emission is high (above the upper limit of the band), it is *not* reinforced; when the stimuli terminate and its force emission is low (descending crossing of threshold), it *is* reinforced.

It might be expected that with progressive training the subjects would learn to cease emitting force immediately upon the onset of the exteroceptive feedback. Although there is undoubtedly such a tendency, the rapidity of behavioral change required may provide a practical limitation: the animal simply may not be able to "respond" fast enough. During a typical response the rate of change of force emission is approximately of the order of .05 gm./millisecond. In 100 milliseconds the animal accordingly passes through a 5-gm. band, a rate that certainly would appear to tax the limits of reaction time. It should be noted that the problem of speed of "response" is peculiar to a feedback stimulus in which onset is characterized by a step function such as those employed here. The animal's own cutaneous and proprioceptive feedback stimuli are undoubtedly continuous.

In general, we have assumed that the introduction of the exteroceptive feedback parallels existing cutaneous and proprioceptive feedback loops.

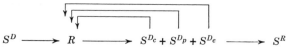

$$S^D \longrightarrow R \longrightarrow S^{D_c} + S^{D_p} + S^{D_e} \longrightarrow S^R$$

Generation of the indicated feedback stimuli "shapes" the response. The paradigm describes a dynamic behavioral process. It is the consequence of this process that we measure when we measure such properties as the peak force of response.

Interference with Feedback [1]

The studies considered thus far in this chapter have shown that the introduction of some systematic exteroceptive correlate of response

[1] The experiment reported in this section was conducted by Theodore Marton as a portion of his doctoral dissertation, Princeton University, 1962.

force modifies that response property. The analogous role of behavior-based feedback has only been inferred. In general, we have assumed that the exteroceptive and proprioceptive feedback loops are parallel, and comparable in function. Of present interest is a study that deals more directly with the behavior-based feedback itself.

The emission of force undoubtedly produces cutaneous stimulation at the organism's point of contact with the manipulandum. Afferent sensory impulses from the skin, pressure receptors, as well as receptors in the active muscles probably all contribute to the feedback complex generated by a lever press. It is also likely that the "shaping" of the response is dependent on the reliable occurrence of these sensory events. The quality of performance should therefore deteriorate if the stimulus complex is changed, that is, if the relation between the physical properties of the response and the sensory feedback is altered. Local anesthetic provides one practical means of experimentally interfering with the afferent impulses of cutaneous origin in the lever-press response.

The anesthetic we used in the experiment that is about to be discussed was procaine hydrochloride. Sollman (1957) noted:

Direct contact with cocaine, procaine and most of the other local anesthetics paralyzes all forms of nervous tissue . . . The susceptibility of the various nerve fibers presents marked and characteristic quantitative differences. Sensory fibers are most easily attacked. By using appropriate dilutions, the paralysis is complete as if the nerve fibers had been severed with a knife.

In addition to its effectiveness, procaine has low toxicity, and subsequent sensory recovery is generally complete.

Anesthetic Control

A group of 16 animals was used in preliminary work to assess the degree of anesthesia related to procaine injection. In consideration of Sperry's (1943) observation that the rat will frequently autoamputate a completely denervated paw, we established a test procedure using procaine with epinephrine hydrochloride, which tends to extend the effective period of the procaine anesthesia. Each animal was injected with epinephrine alone in the right forepaw and epinephrine with procaine in the left. The solutions were administered by subcutaneous injection, 0.05 cc. each to the volar and dorsal aspects of the paw. The epinephrine solution was 0.0001 concentration; half of the animals received a 2 per cent procaine concentration, the other half received a 1 per cent concentration. Seventeen hours after the injections all animals were examined for self-inflicted tissue damage. None was evident in any of the paws injected with epinephrine alone. Seven of the eight animals receiving 2 per cent procaine showed evidence of self-inflicted tissue damage; three or possibly four animals receiving 1 per cent procaine showed comparable damage.

This procedure established that the dosages of procaine were effective and suggested that the difference between the 1 per cent and 2 per cent procaine concentrations in the indicated quantities produced different degrees of denervation.

Feedback Interference Procedure

A 10-to-15-gm. peak-force band criterion was used to establish the behavioral baseline. Each of nine animals was run on this procedure until a stable mode of performance was established.

The test phase of the experiment called for two run sessions for each animal within a single day, providing a "before" and "after" treatment comparison. Each run involved 50 reinforcements under CRF for responses meeting the 10-to-15-gm. band criterion. The two run sessions for each animal were separated by 20 to 30 minutes.

The procedure for procaine administration was as follows:

1. Immediately following the "before" session of 50 reinforcements, the animals were removed from the experimental chamber and placed in a transportable home cage.

2. They were brought to a nearby, well-ventilated laboratory space and placed in a clear glass jar, 9 in. in diameter and 13-in. high, containing a one-in. cube of absorbent toweling saturated with fresh ether. Use of a general anesthetic was found to reduce the over-all trauma of the procaine administration (for experimenter as well as subject). A wire mesh around the toweling prevented the subject from coming in contact with the ether.

3. The animals were kept in a covered jar until signs of Stage III anesthesia were observed, notably (a) a shift from irregular to regular breathing, (b) absence of eye blink upon lash contact, (c) absence of resistance to passive movement, and (d) absence of reflex activity to strong prodding.

4. Immediately after accomplishment of general anesthesia, the animals were removed from the jar and injected in the volar and dorsal

surfaces of each forepaw. Each of the four injections contained 0.05 cc. of procaine, 2 per cent solution.

5. When the injections were completed, artificial respiration was given to hasten recovery from the general anethesia, with continued rapid, rhythmic compression of the abdominal cavity and thoracic cage of the animal until the subject displayed head movements.

6. The subjects were then returned to their home cages. Twenty minutes later, they were reintroduced to the Skinner box.

7. An "after" run of 50 reinforcements at the 10-to-15-gm. band was carried out.

Before the session when procaine was administered, a variety of control sessions was run, exposing subjects to different components of the injection regimen and excluding only the introduction of the procaine itself. The critical control entailed the injection procedure described, except that a saline solution was used instead of procaine. None of the eight control sessions produced a significant change in the proportion of responses that met reinforcement criterion. For each, the data analysis compared the "before" with the "after" performance.

Effects of Feedback Interference

The primary aim of the experimental procedure was an examination of band performance when some components of feedback were eliminated.

During the "before" session, the subjects showed typical peak-force band performance. The group mean for the proportion of responses that fell within the 10-to-15-gm. band was 49.0 per cent; the distribution peaked within the band. Following procaine injection, during the "after" session the group mean proportion of responses that met the criterion dropped to 39.8 per cent. This comparison may be seen in Fig. 7-7. The degree to which the anesthetic reduced the quality of the performance is more readily apparent in Fig. 7-8. In this figure, the difference between the "before" and "after" distributions is plotted directly. The data indicate that by chemically interfering with the afferent sensory impulses, one can produce a specific decrease in the proportion of responses falling within the band. The data for an individual subject are shown in Fig. 7-9; the disruption of performance is obvious.

The group's general tendency toward posttreatment deterioration of performance showed considerable variation from subject to subject. A plot of the difference between the distributions "before" and "after"

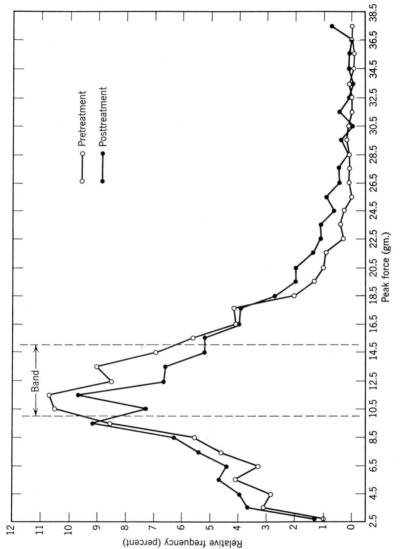

Figure 7-7 Relative frequency distributions of peak force of response during feedback interference with a 10-to-15 gm. peak-force reinforcement band. The distributions reflect group performance preceding and following procaine injection.

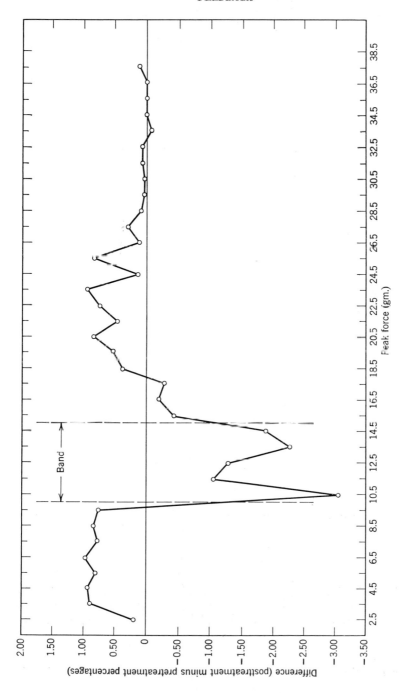

Figure 7-8 Distribution of differences in relative frequency of peak force of response preceding and following procaine injection. This curve plots the differences between the frequency distributions in Fig. 7-7.

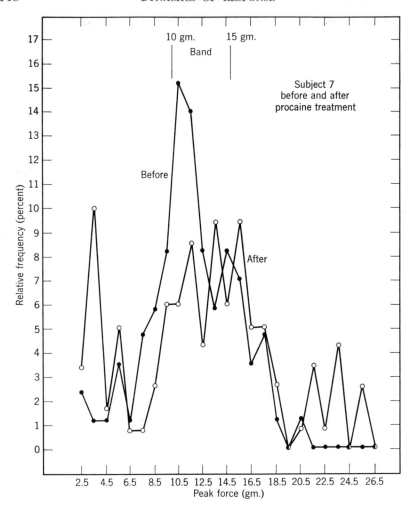

Figure 7-9 Relative frequency distributions of peak force of response for a single subject preceding and following procaine interference with feedback. The reinforcement criterion is 10-to-15 gm. peak force.

procaine injection is shown for each one of the nine subjects in Fig. 7-10. The data for the animals can be characterized according to the following basis of change: *"A,"* a general increase in variability; *"B,"* an increase in low-force responses; and *"C,"* an increase in high-force responses.

The question remains as to what "controls" the force emission in

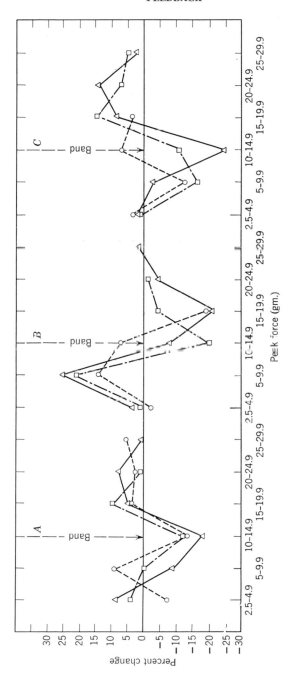

Figure 7-10 Distribution of differences in relative frequency of peak force of response preceding and following procaine injection. Each curve represents an individual subject. Groupings show: (A), decrease in band, increase in above-band and below-band responses; (B), increase in below-band responses; (C), increase in above-band responses.

the absence of cutaneous feedback. It is quite likely that the proprioceptive cues generated at the muscles themselves play a major role in
the activity of these muscles. The present study merely indicates that
performance may be disrupted when there is interference with cutaneous feedback; the role of proprioceptive feedback is much more
difficult to isolate experimentally.

Conclusions

Both the feedback introduction (exteroceptive) and feedback interference (cutaneous) studies considered in this chapter indicate that
manipulation of feedback produces changes in behavior. The general
picture suggests that at every moment the organism's behavior may
produce sensible changes in its external and internal environment.
These changes may in turn provide the effective cues for the behavior
of the next moment. Like any discriminative process, the performance
is shaped by a systematic relation between the stimuli and behavior-
contingent reinforcement. Repeated manifestations of this relation
strengthen the bond. The quality of the performance depends upon
the availability and discriminability of the controlling stimuli.

Chapter Eight

Effort Expenditure and Schedules

CHARACTERISTICS OF RESPONSE maintained under schedules of intermittent reinforcement will be considered in this chapter and the following one. It is well known that there are two major classes of such schedules. "Interval" schedules are procedures that restrict reinforcement eligibility to a specified time of occurrence of the response. "Ratio" schedules restrict reinforcement eligibility on the basis of a specified number of responses. The parameters regarding time and number may be fixed or variable.

It is a principal property of a regimen of intermittent reinforcement, and also of discrimination training, that emission of a criterion response per se is not a sufficient condition for reinforcement. In discrimination training, however, reinforcement eligibility is usually related to some experimentally varied exteroceptive stimulus. Training under the discrimination procedure generally leads to conformity to the conditions established for reinforcement; the organism learns to emit the correct response under the correct condition.

Schedules of intermittent reinforcement tend to produce reliable modes of performance that systematically relate to the parameters of the schedule. Typically, the behavior has been described in terms of the time and frequency of response emission. The general line of analysis that has been followed may be gathered from an introductory statement to Ferster and Skinner's *Schedules of Reinforcement* (1957, p. 3): "The primary purpose of the present book is to present a series of experiments designed to evaluate the extent to which the organism's own behavior enters into the determination of its subsequent behavior."

The notion that the organism's behavior may exert control over subsequent behavior suggests the importance of examining the response itself in detail. Reinforcement-schedule parameters such as interval length and ratio length may systematically affect the rate of response and vary the duration of pauses in responding following reinforcement. One major purpose of the series of experiments reported in this chapter and the next is to determine what systematic variations occur in the intensive properties of the responses themselves.

In addition to the conventional schedule parameters, we also examine the effect of the independent variable, "criterion," on reinforcement schedules that include the differentiation of some response characteristic. The response differentiations in the studies reported in this chapter are based on the $\int F\,dt$ (effort) measure. In ratio schedules, for instance, this procedure makes it possible to specify both the minimum number of responses and the minimum response "effort" required for reinforcement. The total effort of response that must be emitted for each reinforcement may then be varied by manipulation of either the ratio, the criterion, or both. The analysis of the schedule performance includes both examination of the manner in which the subjects meet the schedule requirements and the effects of effort expenditure on subsequent performance. As to the subjects' way of meeting requirements, a new aspect of ratio scheduling is introduced. When a suprathreshold criterion is specified, a given response may or may not reach this value, although every response is quantified along the physical continuum on which the criterion is specified. Consequently, despite the *fixed* ratio and the minimum effort requirement, the response output of the organism on a single ratio cycle is free to vary over a wide range above the minimum. This freedom provides the ratio-scheduling technique with some of the latitude of the dependent variables formerly limited to interval schedules.

The application of a specified reinforcement criterion to an intermittent reinforcement schedule introduces some basic questions concerning response differentiation. It is generally assumed that response "strength" is greater under intermittent reinforcement than under CRF. The basis for this assumption relies on such response measures as resistance to extinction and rate of response (Keller and Schoenfeld, 1950). In the present context we shall approach the notion of "strength" in terms of what kind of responses occur as well as of the frequency of responses. The degree of conformity of the conditioned behavior to the reinforcement criterion may have as appropriate a place in the concept of response strength as does the frequency and temporal distribution of response.

Systematic periods of low response rate (or the limit, pausing) within schedule cycles have been taken as indications of systematic variations in response strength. In the present series of experiments we examine systematic changes in the dimensional properties of individual responses as well. As to the criterion, the relative frequency with which a response meets the requirement provides a quantitative measure of performance. This measure may be used to analyze the control by the criterion over the response properties and to describe the way in which this control varies over the sequence of unreinforced responses within a schedule cycle.

General Method

Each of the interval and ratio schedules was run from nine to 12 days, and a single session comprised 25 to 50 reinforced cycles. Schedule performance was preceded by four days of regular reinforcement at the reinforcement criterion for the first intermittent reinforcement schedule to which the subjects would be exposed. Exceptions to this procedure were subjects 15 and 37, which were run 20 to 35 days on each of their schedules.

A fixed-effort schedule was employed for subjects 72 to 77. Since this procedure was somewhat unusual, the details of method are discussed in the section in which the data are reported (p. 173).

The sequence of schedules for each subject is shown in Table 8-1. Two different criteria may be used in ratio schedules. They are defined as follows: *reinforcement criterion,* the specified response measure that must be met in order for reinforcement to take place, given that all other reinforcement requirements are satisfied; *step criterion,* the specified response measure that must be met in order for the response to achieve a unit advance in the ratio count.

Each criterion may be varied independently, as we have done for animals 15 and 37. In terms of our definitions, the previous literature on ratio reinforcement schedules has invariably concerned schedules in which the step and reinforcement criteria are equal, and both are identical to the response threshold.

The series of fixed-ratio (FR) schedules reported explore the effects of ratio length and reinforcement criterion on the dimensional properties of individual responses. The cumulative $\int F \, dt$ within a cycle is

TABLE 8-1

Experimental Conditions

Subjects	Order	Type of Schedule	Reinforcement Criterion	Step Criterion
2 and 3 *	1	FI 30 sec.	5 gm.-sec.	—
	2	FI 1 min.	5 gm.-sec.	—
	3	FI 2 min.	5 gm.-sec.	—
	4	FI 2 min.	2.5 gm.-sec.	—
	5	FI 2 min.	10 gm.-sec.	—
	6	VI 2 min.	10 gm.-sec.	—
1 and 8 *	1	FR 6	5 gm.-sec.	5 gm.-sec.
	2	FR 12	5 gm.-sec.	5 gm.-sec.
	3	FR 24	5 gm.-sec.	5 gm.-sec.
	4	FR 6	threshold	threshold
6 and 7 *	1	FR 6	10 gm.-sec.	10 gm.-sec.
	2	FR 12	10 gm.-sec.	10 gm.-sec.
	3	FR 12	5 gm.-sec.	5 gm.-sec.
	4	FR 24	2.5 gm.-sec.	2.5 gm.-sec.
11 and 12 *	1	FR 6	threshold	threshold
	2	FR 12	threshold	threshold
	3	FR 24	threshold	threshold
15 and 37	1	FR 12	5 gm.-sec.	threshold
	2	FR 12	8 gm.-sec.	threshold
	3	FR 15	threshold	threshold
72 to 77	1	CRF	threshold	—
	2	Fixed Effort	30 gm.-sec.	—

* Each subject had four days of CRF at the reinforcement criterion for the first intermittent schedule prior to entering the tabulated sequence.

taken as an index of the effort expenditure in the conditioned behavior. This measure subsumes the force and the duration of individual responses, as well as the frequency of response.[1]

Two methodological considerations enter our programming and analysis of FR. The first concerns the specification of criteria, as dis-

[1] A fuller discussion of the implications of the $\int F\,dt$ as a behavioral measure is presented in Chapter 1.

cussed; the second concerns the distribution of total response effort per reinforcement. Thus, when the "step criterion" is specified in $\int F\, dt$ units, the total effort required within a ratio cycle may be distributed by different combinations of ratio length and step criterion. In the present design, for instance, FR 6 (10 gram-seconds), FR 12 (5 gram-seconds), and FR 24 (2.5 gram-seconds) all require a minimum of 60 gram-seconds for reinforcement. The terms in parentheses indicate both the step and reinforcement criteria.

Results

Fixed Ratio Length

A fixed-ratio schedule parameter that has been the subject of considerable experimental investigation (Ferster and Skinner, 1957; Boren, 1961) has been the ratio length itself. Such behavioral characteristics as the rate of response and the duration of the postreinforcement pause have been demonstrated to be affected by the ratio length.

Four subjects performed under FR 6, FR 12 and FR 24, with the step criterion and the reinforcement criterion equal and constant for all schedules. Animals 1 and 8 performed with a 5-gram-second criterion (step and reinforcement); animals 11 and 12 performed with both criteria equal to the response threshold (2.5-gm. peak force).

In Fig. 8-1 the mean total effort per reinforcement (A) and the mean $\int F\, dt$ per response (B) are shown. With the change in schedule, there is—for all four subjects—a monotonic rise in the total effort per reinforcement with an increase in ratio length. The animals performing at the threshold criterion exert effort considerably below the level of the 5-gram-second criterion animals. Nevertheless, the performance of the latter should be considered in relation to the minimum effort required by the schedule (shown in Fig. 8-1-A). This minimum is a linear function of the schedule length. A negative acceleration in the performance functions is suggested for the two 5-gram-second subjects.

Figure 8-1-B indicates that the mean $\int F\, dt$ for individual responses did not rise with an increase in ratio length for subjects 1 and 8 (5-gram-second criterion), but an increase with ratio length *is* shown for subjects 11 and 12 (threshold criterion). (FR 24 is significantly different from FR 6 at the 5 per cent level, Kolmogorov-Smirnov two-tailed test.) Although a greater number of responses is a major factor

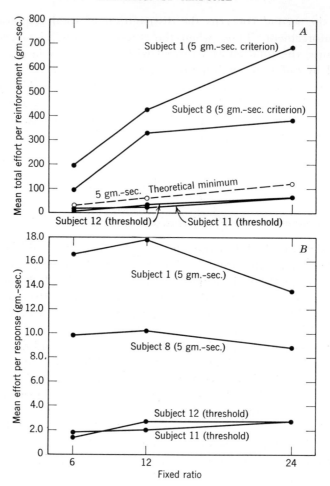

Figure 8-1 Mean total effort per reinforcement (*A*), and mean response effort as a function of fixed ratio length (*B*). The criterion for step advance and reinforcement is 5 gm.-sec. for subjects 1 and 8, and threshold (2.5-gm. peak force) for subjects 11 and 12. The dashed line in (*A*) indicates the theoretical minimum effort per reinforcement with the 5-gm.-sec. criterion, appropriate to subjects 1 and 8 only.

contributing to greater effort per reinforcement on longer schedules, the threshold criterion animals show that mean $\int F\,dt$ per response can also contribute to an effort increase with an increase in ratio length.

The percentage of total responses meeting the 5-gram-second crite-

TABLE 8-2

Per Cent of Total Responses Meeting Criterion

		Subjects	
Schedule		1	8
FR 6	5 gm.-sec.	52.0	62.1
FR 12	5 gm.-sec.	51.9	38.3
FR 24	5 gm.-sec.	47.1	57.4

rion is recorded in Table 8-2 for subjects 1 and 8. As with the mean $\int F\, dt$ per response, no systematic change with schedule length is evident. The characteristics of individual responses in terms of their likelihood of meeting the criterion and of their mean $\int F\, dt$ are not affected by schedule length for those subjects required to meet a relatively high $\int F\, dt$ criterion. With the threshold criterion, the effect of the schedule length apparently tends to be reflected in the mean $\int F\, dt$ per response.

The distinction between the effect of schedule length on performance under the two different criteria (threshold and 5 gram-seconds) probably relates to the level of $\int F\, dt$ generated by each requirement. The situation is comparable with the data reported in Chapter 3, where it is demonstrated that the increase in the peak force, duration, and time integral of force of response during extinction was small or even absent when the level during reinforced performance was already high.

The Effect of Criterion

Several comparisons are available to demonstrate the performance of a single animal at a fixed FR value for which the criterion is varied. The mean $\int F\, dt$ per response for all of these performances is shown in Table 8-3. In each case the step criterion and the reinforcement criterion were equal.

For every animal, an increase in the criterion produced an increase in the $\int F\, dt$. The criteria were all based on $\int F\, dt$, with the exception of threshold. For threshold, the minimum $\int F\, dt$ was unspecified, but may be considered approximately zero.

It is likely that the effect of increase is directly attributable to the

TABLE 8-3

Mean Integral of Force per Response for Animals Performing at the Same Fixed Ratio under Two Different Criteria (gm.-sec.)

	FR 6			FR 12	
	Subjects				Subjects	
Criterion	1	8	Criterion	6	7
Threshold	5.3	3.6	5 gm.-sec.	5.3	8.1
5 gm.-sec.	16.5	9.8	10 gm.-sec.	13.3	11.3

control exerted by the criterion itself (that is, differentiation) rather than to some coincidental controlling factor such as number of unreinforced responses per ratio cycle. For animal 6 (Table 8-3, FR 12), the mean number of responses per ratio cycle was actually lower for the 10-gram-second criterion, but this criterion nonetheless produced a higher mean integral of force than did the 5-gram-second criterion. Additional relevant data were indicated in the previous section; with a 5-gram-second criterion, it was shown that the mean $\int F\, dt$ did not systematically vary with ratio length.

Equal Effort Ratios

Two subjects were run on three different ratio-criterion combinations that required identical cumulative effort expenditures. The total effort requirement in each was 60 gram-seconds per reinforcement. The schedules were FR 6 (10 gram-seconds), FR 12 (5 gram-seconds), and FR 24 (2.5 gram-seconds). These schedules lend themselves to an analysis of the relative contributions of schedule length and criterion to FR performance.

The total effort per reinforcement for the three schedules is plotted as a function of ratio length in Fig. 8-2-*A*. It can be seen that for the two shorter ratios (FR 6 and 12) there is little difference in the total effort expenditure, but the longest ratio combined with the lowest criterion produces an increase in the total emitted response effort.

For each schedule both a minimum number of responses and a minimum $\int F\, dt$ for each effective response are specified. Some indication of the degree to which these requirements are met is shown in Fig.

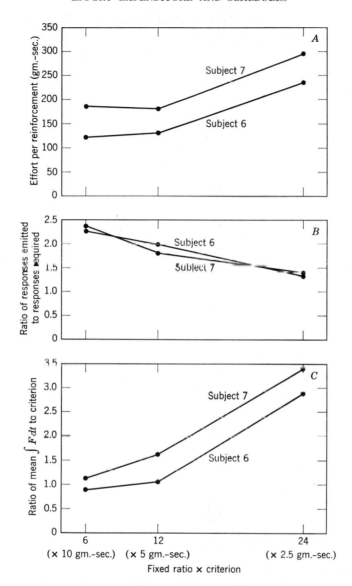

Figure 8-2   Mean effort per reinforcement (*A*), ratio of number of responses emitted to minimum number of responses required (*B*), and ratio of mean response effort to effort criterion (*C*) as a function of reinforcement schedule for subjects 6 and 7. The abscissa is scaled in fixed ratio length, which was varied inversely with the criterion for step advance and reinforcement (noted below the ratio).

8-2-*B* and -*C*. The curves in part *B* of the figure indicate a progressive decrease in the relative frequency of extra or subcriterion responses with an increase in ratio length (and a related reduction in the criterion). The two curves in part *C* of Fig. 8-2 show both a positive slope and a positive inflection. They indicate that the reduction in the criterion did not produce a proportionate reduction in the mean $\int F \, dt$. Although both subjects showed an absolute drop in the mean $\int F \, dt$ from FR 6 (10 gram-seconds) to FR 12 (5 gram-seconds), an increase over the latter occurred for the FR 24 (2.5-gram-second) schedule (5.3 gram-seconds to 7.3 gram-seconds for animal 6; 8.1 to 8.6 gram-seconds for animal 7). In this instance the schedule length appears to exert control over the mean $\int F \, dt$.

The general conclusion suggested by the data is that there is an interaction between schedule length and the criteria in determining the mean $\int F \, dt$ of response emission. The effect of the schedule length is most apparent when the criterion itself is low (threshold and 2.5 gram-seconds). With higher criteria (5 gram-seconds and 10 gram-seconds), schedule length is less likely to affect differentially the mean $\int F \, dt$ per response.

Effort and Postreinforcement Pauses

It is widely recognized that schedules of fixed (interval or ratio) intermittent reinforcement typically lead to a reduced likelihood of response immediately following reinforcement. This phenomenon has been attributed to the discriminative aspects of the schedule (Ferster and Skinner, 1957). In the period immediately following reinforcement, the likelihood of reinforcement (and therefore response) is least.

Data in the present study show that the postreinforcement pause in responding is influenced by the criterion as well as by the schedule length. When a constant criterion was applied over different FRs, we found the typical progressive increase in the duration of the pause with an increase in the FR length. The mean duration of postreinforcement pauses under the various schedules is shown in Table 8-4. In addition to the effect of ratio length, there is a marked effect related to the criterion. It is interesting to observe that doubling the effort requirement per response (5 gram-seconds to 10 gram-seconds) for FR 12 results in an approximately doubled pause duration for both subjects. These longer pauses with the 10-gram-second criterion can not be attributed to a greater number of unreinforced responses. For animal 6, the FR 12 (10-gram-second) schedule in fact produced

TABLE 8-4

Mean Length of Postreinforcement Pause in Responding
(minutes)

| | 5-gm.-sec. Criterion | | Equal-Effort Ratios | | |
| | Subjects | | Subjects | | |
Fixed Ratio	1	8	6	7	
6	0.78	0.18	0.94	0.43	(10 gm.-sec.)
12	1.00	0.31	1.50	0.63	(5 gm.-sec.)
24	1.42	0.92	2.00	0.63	(2.5 gm.-sec.)

Fixed Ratio Constant

| FR 6 | | | FR 12 | | |
| | Subjects | | | Subjects | |
Criterion	1	8	Criterion	6	7
Threshold	0.30	0.07	5 gm.-sec.	1.50	0.63
5 gm.-sec.	0.78	0.18	10 gm.-sec.	3.18	1.13

fewer responses per cycle than did the FR 12 (5-gram-second) schedule. For animal 7 this was not true, but for this subject the number
of responses per cycle for the FR 24 (2.5-gram-second) schedule was
greater than the number under FR 12 (10 gram-seconds), and the
latter produced considerably longer pauses, 1.13 minutes as compared
to 0.63 minute.[2]

These data make it apparent that the independent variable, criterion, can exert control over the temporal occurrence of response. The
postreinforcement pause may be described as a period during which
the momentary response strength is low. The discriminative role of
reinforcement in setting the occasion for the pause relates to the behavior required for reinforcement. Both the ratio and the criterion
contribute to this requirement. The common denominator appears to

---

[2] Among the FI schedules, the pause in responding following reinforcement did *not*
vary systematically with the criterion. This distinction between ratio and interval
schedules suggests that interval pausing is less under the direct control of the response emission that precedes reinforcement.

be some measure of total behavioral output. We have attempted to specify this by the measure of individual responses we have termed "effort" ($\int F\, dt$) and by the cumulation of this quantity, thereby taking into account the response-frequency measure as well.

It may be noted that Schoenfeld, Cumming, and Hearst (1956) have demonstrated a means of controlling pause duration through the manipulation of certain temporal parameters of a reinforcement schedule. In subsequent studies it was shown that although there was no direct change in requirement for reinforcement (that is, the requirement was always a single response with presumably a constant criterion), those schedules producing more responses (greater behavioral output) tended to produce longer pauses (Hearst, 1958; Clark, 1959).

The exact contribution of the behavior output appears to be related to a discriminative process. Pauses are likely to occur only when the organism has been exposed to a regimen in which a reinforcement immediately following a reinforcement is highly improbable. Variable ratio schedules, for instance, may produce no substantial pausing even though they require more responses for reinforcement than do FR schedules that show regular postreinforcement pauses. The absence of pauses despite high requirements suggests that the role of effort expenditure in the performance can not be interpreted in terms only of some form of physiological fatigue. Rather, it is likely that consistent effort expenditure allows for the organism's discrimination of its own behavior. Ferster and Skinner (1957) suggest that response acquires the function of a discriminative stimulus in schedule performance. Extending this notion, some intensive property of the response (such as the $\int F\, dt$ or peak force) can provide the necessary stimulus basis for the discrimination.

Since the effect of cumulated effort expenditure is to produce directly related postreinforcement pause duration, the distinction between response strength before and after reinforcement may also be said to depend on the cumulated effort expenditure. The function is discriminative. With a passage of time the organism again begins responding. The phenomenon is approximated by Hull's early reactive inhibition postulate (1943, p. 300), which inversely relates the momentary likelihood of response to the "number" of antecedent responses and the "work" involved. He further states that the inhibition thus generated dissipates as a function of time. Although our observations neither confirm nor disagree with the quantitative attributes of Hull's postulate, we have in fact demonstrated the control of schedule performance that is exerted by an energy-expenditure variable.[3]

Response Strength and Within-Cycle Effects

In discussing postreinforcement pauses, lack of response has been taken to indicate reduced response strength. Stated in other terms, the lack of response is implicit evidence that some behavior other than the measured response has sufficient relative strength to preclude response emission. The relation between this competing behavior and the measured response is generally unknown.

With several of the FR schedules presently under discussion, the FR is based on a criterion defining a subclass of the generic response class. Nevertheless, all responses were measured. With this procedure it is possible to specify the empirical likelihood that a response will achieve the criterion value for each ordinal position constituting a ratio cycle. The convention we have followed has been to consider the ratio cycle as beginning with a reinforced response and terminating with the unreinforced response preceding the beginning of the next cycle. The likelihood that any particular response will meet the criterion constitutes a measure that may appropriately be considered "response strength."

A Roman numeral denotes the reinforced response. The unreinforced cycle positions are indicated by Arabic numerals. For instance, the first unreinforced criterion response of a ratio cycle is specified as 1, the second as 2, etc. The likelihood of a *criterion* response for ordinal position 1 is determined by the mean number of *all* responses emitted by the subject in achieving the first unreinforced step of the ratio cycle. The probability of criterion response as a function of ordinal position is shown for subjects 6 and 7 in Fig. 8-3 and for subjects 1 and 8 in Fig. 8-4. A characteristic pattern is suggested; it is most obvious for subject 6. Immediately following reinforcement the probability of achieving criterion is low. Successive ordinal positions show a progressive increase in the likelihood of achieving criterion.

Despite the individual differences among the four subjects, only subject 8 does not show a decided tendency toward low probability of criterion response in its first response after reinforcement (position 1). Such a low probability is shown on all three schedules for subjects

---

[3] In the present discussion we persist with the contention that effort more than work is a variable of interest in the analysis of behavior; see Chapter 1.

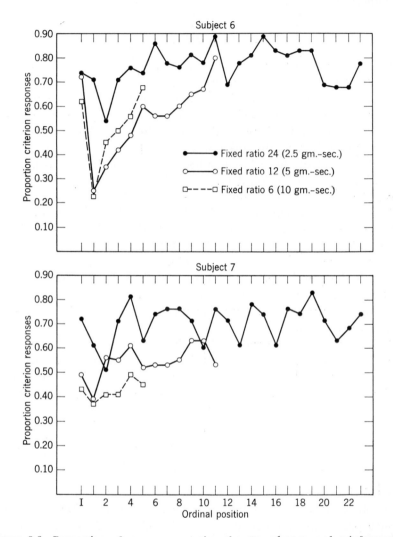

Figure 8-3 Proportion of responses meeting the step-advance and reinforcement criterion (1/mean number of responses to advance in ratio) as a function of ordinal position within the fixed ratio for subjects 6 and 7. The Roman numeral indicates the reinforced response.

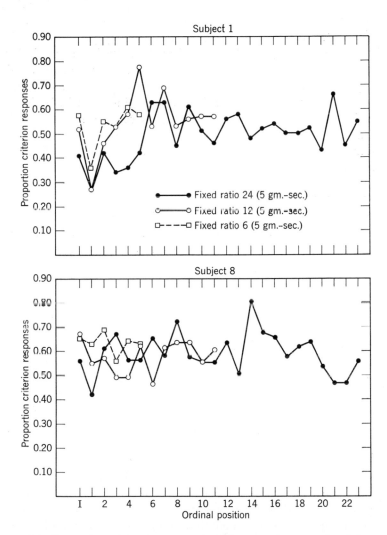

Figure 8-4 Proportion of responses meeting the step-advance and reinforcement criterion (1/mean number of responses to advance in ratio) as a function of ordinal position within the fixed ratio for subjects 1 and 8. The Roman numeral indicates the reinforced response.

1 and 6. For subject 7, on FR 24 (2.5 gram-seconds), it is ordinal position 2, rather than 1, that shows the least probability of achieving criterion. For subject 8, only the longest FR schedule shows a function similar to the general pattern evidenced by the other subjects.

If we take the likelihood of meeting the criterion as an index of response strength, we find that there are systematic changes within a ratio cycle. Reinforcement lowers the relative frequency of criterion responses, and progressive nonreinforcement increases it. This observation is comparable with the observations concerning FR schedules that have been made in terms of response rate. Immediately following reinforcement, response strength is lowest (pauses occur). Subsequently, the subject may immediately enter, or accelerate to, a high rate of response that persists until the next reinforcement takes place (Ferster and Skinner, 1957).

For illustrative purposes, cumulative response records for FR 24 (2.5 gram-seconds) are shown in Fig. 8-5. Both subjects show regular postreinforcement pauses. Both subjects also show negative as well as positive accelerations in the rate of response within a cycle. These negative accelerations may be a special property of FR schedules with high step and reinforcement criteria. The progressive increase in the likelihood of meeting the criterion generally corresponds to an increase in response duration. Long response duration in turn may contribute to a declining response rate.

Portions of the cumulative response records for subjects 6 and 7 under FR 12 (10 gram-seconds) are also included in Fig. 8-5. The extraordinarily long postreinforcement pauses following runs of relatively few responses (but high effort) are apparent.

Both postreinforcement pauses and the low relative frequency of criterion responses in the initial cycle positions provide a consistent description of a systematic reduction in response strength within a cycle during FR performance. Nevertheless, the increase in the likelihood of criterion response emission as the reinforced cycle position is approached could possibly be explained as a direct effect of extinction. In Chapter 3 it was seen that nonreinforcement typically produces an increase in the peak force, duration, and $\int F\, dt$ of response; possible explanations were offered in Chapter 5. In Chapter 9 this phenomenon is also demonstrated during a variety of FR schedules in which the step and reinforcement criteria are both at threshold. The threshold criterion provides, of course, a regimen in which the probability that a response will meet the criterion must be 1.0. Consequently, an elevation in emitted $\int F\, dt$ does not necessarily represent

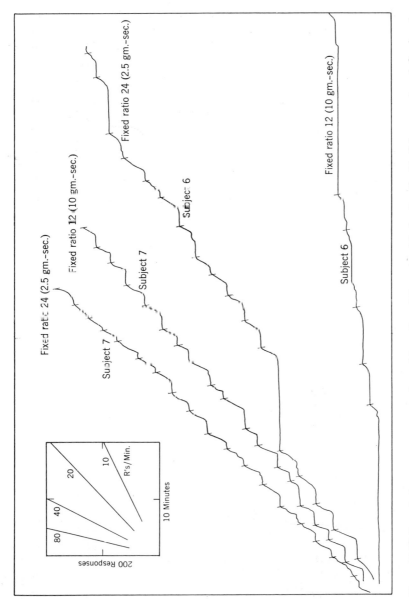

Figure 8-5 Cumulative response curves for subjects 6 and 7, each with fixed ratio 24 (2.5 gm.-sec.) and fixed ratio 12 (10 gm.-sec.).

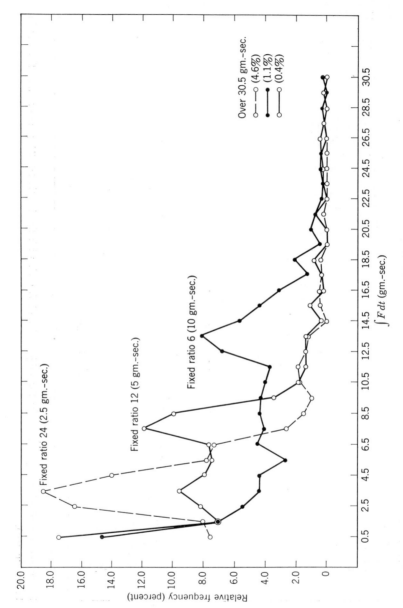

Figure 8-6 Relative frequency distributions of response effort for subject 6 under a set of Equal-effort ratios. Note how the peaking of the distribution corresponds in each case to the criterion.

an increase in response strength (unless the elevation represents a shift away from below-threshold—and unmeasured—behavioral events).

The question of the analysis of the progressive elevation of the $\int F\,dt$ of response within a ratio cycle relates to the general problem of the maintenance of a differentiation with intermittent reinforcement. One interesting problem for future experimentation is the maintenance of a "band" differentiation on ratio or interval reinforcement. With the "band," an increase in the magnitude of the differentiated measure does not necessarily increase the likelihood of a subject's meeting the criterion. The usefulness of this procedure would be that the effect of the criterion and the effect of extinction need not be confounded.

Subject 6 in the present experiment provided good evidence for the direct effect of the criterion on response effort. The relative frequency distributions of $\int F\,dt$ for subject 6 are shown in Fig. 8-6. Despite the sequential effects depicted in Fig. 8-3-A, all three schedules produced distribution peaks that relate to the respective criteria. The distributions for this subject's FR performance, in fact, indicate more direct control by the criterion than was observed for many subjects differentiated on $\int F\,dt$ with regular reinforcement. Nevertheless, the other FR subjects did *not* show this peaking. For the present, the performance of animal 6 must be considered an unusual demonstration of the maintenance of effort differentiation with intermittent reinforcement.

Separation of Step and Reinforcement Criterion

The FR schedules thus far discussed had identical step and reinforcement criteria within any schedule. Two subjects were run under three FR schedules in which different reinforcement criteria were used, but the step criterion was kept at response threshold. Under this procedure, after a fixed number of responses of any value are emitted, reinforcement eligibility is established. The reinforcement eligibility continues until a response of the required magnitude (reinforcement criterion) occurs. Although responses below the reinforcement criterion are effective in advancing the subject to the cycle position in which reinforcement may take place, such responses never directly produce reinforcement.

In Fig. 8-7 the percentage of responses for each cycle position that exceeded the *reinforcement* criterion are shown. In cycle position I, the reinforced position, the proportion represents the reciprocal of

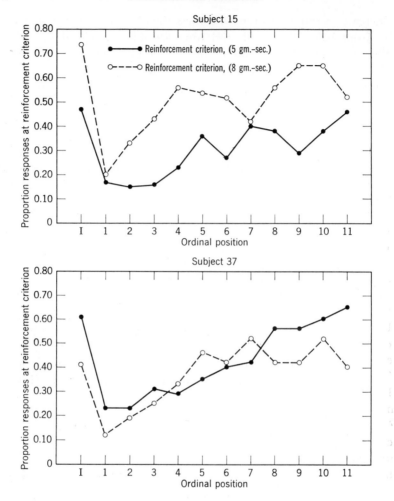

Figure 8-7 Proportion of responses meeting the reinforcement criterion as a function of ordinal position within the fixed ratio for subjects 15 and 37. The criterion for step advance in the ratio is threshold (2.5-gm. peak force). However, at the end of the unreinforced run, a response meeting the indicated reinforcement criterion was required. The Roman numeral denotes the reinforced ratio position.

the mean number of responses the subject emitted after reinforcement eligibility had been established. For all the other cycle positions the percentage represents the relative frequency with which the response that achieved that cycle position actually exceeded the reinforcement criterion. It should be remembered that reaching the reinforcement criterion was not a schedule requirement except when the ratio count had been completed. Within the cycle both subjects on both schedules displayed a progressive increase in the likelihood of emitting a response exceeding the reinforcement criterion.

The question may again be raised concerning the basis of the observed within-cycle changes in performance. Although there is no magnitude requirement for the unreinforced responses that count off the ratio steps, the magnitude increases. Either of the two following circumstances may be applicable to an understanding of this phenomenon: the increase in the $\int F\,dt$ occurs in direct relation to the number of successive unreinforced responses that have occurred and may therefore reflect the "extinction effect"; a response of criterion magnitude becomes more likely as the subject approaches the cycle position in which such a response is required.

In order to examine the effect of the reinforcement criterion, we ran both animals on FR 15 schedules with both the step criterion and the reinforcement criterion at threshold (2.5-gm. peak force, minimum $\int F\,dt$). FR 15 was chosen because it provided unreinforced series of responses that were *longer* than the mean number of responses the subjects emitted in the two previous schedules. (FR 12 schedules with the 5-gram-second and 8 gram second reinforcement criteria produced mean cycle lengths of between 12.5 and 13.5 responses.)

Table 8-5 contains the mean $\int F\,dt$ on all three schedules for both subjects. Although the longest unreinforced sequences of responses occurred on the FR 15 schedule, this schedule produced the lowest mean $\int F\,dt$ for each subject. Animal 15 shows a reversal of the criterion effect for 5 gram-seconds and 8 gram-seconds. Examination of the raw data suggests that despite the lower criterion on the 5-gram-second schedule, the actual $\int F\,dt$ values that occurred for reinforced responses

TABLE 8-5

Mean $\int F\,dt$ (gm.-sec.) for Subjects Exposed to Schedules in Which the Reinforcement Criterion Is Greater Than or Equal to the Threshold

Schedule	Step Criterion	Reinforcement Criterion	Subjects 15	37
FR 12	threshold	5 gm.-sec.	14.5	9.0
FR 12	threshold	8 gm.-sec.	9.4	11.7
FR 15	threshold	threshold	6.9	4.3

were not lower on this schedule. It must be remembered that a contingency change can be effective only if the range of variation in performance makes it likely that different behavior will be reinforced. The reduction of the criterion to threshold, on the other hand, provided the circumstances in which very low values of $\int F\,dt$ (less than 1.0 gram-second) were frequently reinforced. This condition appears to have produced a differentiation of lower $\int F\,dt$ values.

It is again apparent that both the criteria and the sequences of unreinforced responses contribute to the level of $\int F\,dt$ that are observed.[4] Even though a higher level of $\int F\,dt$ is required only in the reinforced cycle position, the effect of this differentiation may be observed in the entire behavior output of the subject.

A Cumulative Fixed-Effort Schedule [5]

Thus far we have considered schedules in which the properties of individual responses contribute independently to the experimental contingency (step advance or reinforcement). However, it is possible to cumulate such response properties as $\int F\,dt$ or duration over a sequence of responses. The cumulative fixed-effort schedule illustrates this procedure.

In the fixed-effort schedule examined, the schedule criterion was 30 gram-second $\int F\,dt$. Unlike the simple differentiation of $\int F\,dt$ in which a single response must meet the criterion, in the fixed-effort schedule the $\int F\,dt$ of each response is cumulated. Reinforcement takes place at the end of the first response during which the cumulated effort reaches criterion. The animal may be reinforced for a single response ($\geqq 30$ gram-seconds) or he may be reinforced for a sequence of less "effortful" responses when the total effort reaches criterion. This schedule differs from the equal-effort schedules in the following two important respects: no restriction as to number of responses is imposed; no effort is "lost." In the equal-effort schedules, a response that was below criterion made *no* contribution to the achievement of reinforcement; in the cumulative fixed-effort schedule, there is no criterion for a single response—any effort manifested, no matter how small, contributes to the achievement of the reinforcement criterion.

[4] In the following chapter the effects of reinforced and unreinforced sequences of responses are examined in greater detail.

[5] The fixed-effort schedule was studied by Maxwell A. Morfield. The data in this section are based on his master's essay, Princeton University, 1963.

The Cumulative Fixed-Effort Procedure

The six animals used in this study were initially trained under CRF with a threshold (2.5-gm. peak force) reinforcement criterion. This training was carried out for 13 days. The animals were subsequently given 20 days of Fixed-Effort (FE) training with a 30-gram-second criterion. The $\int F\,dt$ for each response was cumulated until the sum reached 30 gram-seconds. At the termination of the response during which this criterion was reached, the subject was reinforced; the cumulative effort storage was reset to zero. Consequently, the next response corresponded to the beginning of a new FE cycle. The animals were run until they had received 35 reinforcements each day during both CRF and FE training.

Cumulative Fixed-Effort Performance

The data resulting from this schedule are shown in Table 8-6. A comparison between response rates for CRF and FE indicates that the response rate increased for every subject during FE. The reinforce-

TABLE 8-6

Response Rates during CRF and Response Rates, Reinforcement Rates, and Per Cent of Responses 30 gm.-sec. or Greater during Fixed Effort *

Measures	Subjects					
	72	73	74	75	76	77
CRF						
Response rate (responses/min.)	7.5	8.4	10.0	7.3	5.3	7.8
Fixed Effort, 30 gm.-sec.						
Response rate (responses/min.)	9.3	10.2	10.7	21.1	7.5	14.0
Reinforcement rate (reinforcements/min.)	5.1	4.9	6.2	5.2	5.3	7.0
Per cent responses $\geq$ 30 gm.-sec.	54	41	54	16	57	44

* All data are means of last three days of CRF and Fixed-Effort schedules, respectively.

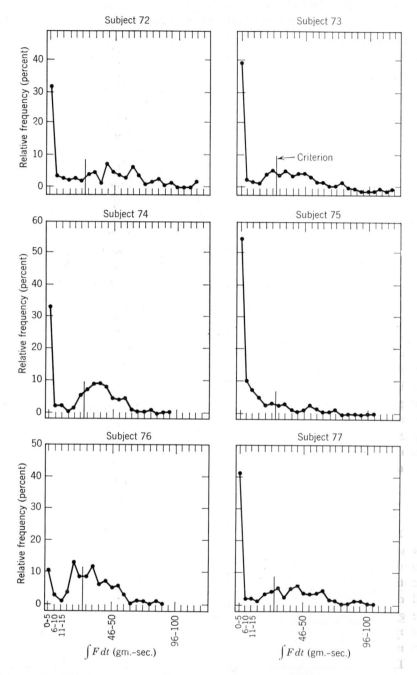

Figure 8-8 Relative frequency distributions of response effort for 6 subjects performing with a cumulative fixed-effort (30 gm.-sec.) reinforcement criterion. The vertical line in each distribution indicates the value of the criterion.

ment rate, however, stayed approximately equal or decreased. Concurrent with the increase in response rate was a remarkable increase in the effortfulness of the individual responses. Table 8-6 shows that 16 per cent to 57 per cent of the responses during FE were greater than 30 gram-seconds. During CRF responses exceeding 5 gram-seconds were quite rare, and those exceeding 10 gram-seconds were essentially nonexistent.

The distribution of $\int F\, dt$ during Fixed-Effort performance is shown in Fig. 8-8. A general tendency to bimodality is evident. Except for animal 75, the distributions show some measure of peaking that relates to the schedule criterion, 30 gram-seconds. Low-effort responses were also maintained with a high relative frequency.

Although the subjects could receive reinforcement with behavior characterized by low-effort responses, the probability of reinforcement for a given response was positively related to the effort magnitude. For instance, 100 per cent of the responses exceeding 30 gram-seconds were necessarily reinforced. Low-effort responses were reinforced only if they followed a sequence of responses that had an effort sum just slightly below the 30-gram-second criterion. The conditions of the schedule appear to maintain both modes of behavior. It should be noted additionally that this particular schedule generated considerably higher values of $\int F\, dt$ than did any of the FR schedules including, for instance, the equal-effort FR that required 60 gram-seconds per reinforcement. However, none of the other schedules placed a premium on high-effort responses. In these other schedules, the animal was most efficient when its effort output was at the level of the criterion for individual responses.

Interval Schedules

Two animals were run on a series of fixed and variable interval schedules (FI and VI). The procedure was similar to the usual interval scheduling, except that a response had to meet the specified criterion of effort in order to be reinforced. These schedules were conducted with an unlimited hold, so that the period of reinforcement eligibility (t^D) continued until a criterion response occurred and the subject was reinforced. Reinforcement initiated the next interval of reinforcement ineligibility (t^Δ).

The mean time integral of force for each subject under the several schedules is shown in Table 8-7. The control exerted by the criterion is apparent. Although there was no systematic change in mean $\int F\, dt$

TABLE 8-7

Mean Time Integral of Force (gm.-sec.) for FI and VI Schedules

Subjects	Fixed Interval (min.)	Criterion (gm.-sec.)		
		2.5	5.0	10.0
2	2.0	4.7	7.7	8.1
	1.0		7.1	
	.5		7.6	
3	2.0	3.8	6.7	8.3
	1.0		7.3	
	.5		5.8	
	Variable Interval (min.)			
2	2.0			14.0
3	2.0			11.6

across the FI schedules at 5 gram-seconds, an increase in the criterion at FI 2 produced an increase in the mean of the $\int F\,dt$ distributions. Of interest is the effect indicated for the VI 2 (10-gram-second) schedule, which led to higher means than for the comparable FI 2 (10-gram-second) schedule.

One characteristic of interval schedules is that a change in the temporal parameters does not change the minimum behavioral output necessary for each reinforcement. A single criterion response at the end of each interval will produce reinforcement. Nevertheless, the *total* behavioral output varies with the temporal parameters of the schedule and with the reinforcement criterion. As with FR, the measure we have taken as an index of this total behavioral output is the cumulative $\int F\,dt$ within an interval. This measure provides an index of the manipulandum-oriented effort expenditure of the subject. This "effort-per-reinforcement" measure is shown for the two subjects in Fig. 8-9. It can be seen that both lengthening the interval and increasing the criterion produce an increase in the effort expenditure. Since the mean $\int F\,dt$ per response did not systematically increase with an increase in interval length (Table 8-7), the effort increase is here attributable to a greater number of responses in the longer intervals. The effort increase with the criterion change (FI 2, Fig. 8-9-*A*), on the other hand, relates to an increase in the mean $\int F\,dt$ per response. Of

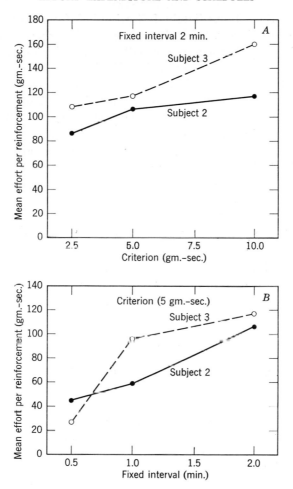

Figure 8-9 Mean effort per reinforcement for subjects 2 and 3 as a function of: (*A*) reinforcement criterion, fixed interval of 2 min. held constant; (*B*) fixed interval, with 5 gm.-sec. reinforcement criterion held constant.

the three FI 2 schedules, the 2.5-gram-second criterion, in fact, produced the highest response rates for both subjects, although the effort expenditure for each was lowest.

Within-Interval Effects

It has frequently been demonstrated that within a single interval of an FI schedule, the likelihood of response occurrence shows systematic variation. Immediately following reinforcement, the likelihood of response is low. With the passage of time there is an increase in the probability that a response will occur. This postreinforcement pause in responding is characteristic of both FR and FI performance.

In the FR schedules, we have shown that a systematic increase in response magnitude occurs across the unreinforced sequence of responses within a cycle. In the following chapter, this FR phenomenon is explored in greater detail.

Examination of within-cycle performance for the two subjects run on interval schedules reveals some interesting differences between the results generated by ratio and those generated by interval schedules. In general, there appears to be greater homogeneity in the effort of response during nonreinforced response sequences of interval schedules. The analysis is based upon a comparison of the mean $\int F\,dt$ for the first two with that of the last two unreinforced responses within the period of reinforcement ineligibility (t^Δ). (In computing the means, only those intervals containing 4 or more t^Δ responses were considered.) The means are shown in Table 8-8. The data are listed sequen-

TABLE 8-8

Mean $\int F\,dt$ (gm.-sec.) for Responses Preceding and Following Reinforcement

		Subject 2				Subject 3			
		First Day		Last Day		First Day		Last Day	
Sequence	Schedule	After S^R	Before S^R	After S^R	Before S^R	After S^R	Before S^R	After S^R	Before S^R
1	FI 0.5 (5 gm.-sec.)	10.6	19.8	9.3	8.5	7.9	14.9	6.3	6.6
2	FI 1 (5 gm.-sec.)	7.4	10.4	7.0	8.5	7.1	8.6	6.3	6.4
3	FI 2 (5 gm.-sec.)	7.2	10.9	5.1	11.0	6.7	7.7	8.3	6.0
4	FI 2 (2.5 gm.-sec.)	5.4	7.5	4.0	4.7	3.1	7.0	3.4	3.5
5	FI 2 (10 gm.-sec.)	6.8	7.6	7.8	9.2	4.6	6.2	7.4	6.5
6	VI 2 (10 gm.-sec.)	4.5	9.2	11.8	15.8	6.8	6.4	8.8	10.6

tially for the first and last days of performance on each schedule. "After S^R" and "Before S^R" refer to the first two and last two t^Δ responses, respectively.

Considering only the FI schedules, the differences between the means of "after" and "before" are not significant (5% level, two-tailed t-test) for either animal on either the first or the last days of the schedules. Nevertheless, both subjects showed a general tendency to make greater response effort before reinforcement than after reinforcement on the first day of exposure to each schedule.

The following general phenomena are suggested by the data in Table 8-8:

1. The difference between the mean $\int F\, dt$ before and after S^R decreases with progressive training on a particular FI schedule.

2. A change to a new schedule with a more restrictive contingency (longer FI or higher criterion) produces a temporary increase in the mean $\int F\, dt$. The effect appears greater for the "before" than for the "after" S^R responses.

3. The "before S^R" responses (generally occurring in close temporal proximity to the onset of t^D) show conformity to the reinforcement criterion after extended training on a schedule.

4. VI training appears to maintain or increase the distinction between "before" and "after" responses, unlike FI training in which the tendency is toward within-interval homogeneity.

It was seen in Chapter 3 that nonreinforcement of a response produces an increase in the vigor of that response. The interesting distinction between FR and FI performance is that FR leads to an entrenchment of this phenomenon, exhibited as a cyclical increase in response vigor. FI, on the other hand, appears to provide the conditions in which the increase in response magnitude following nonreinforcement diminishes with training. The data also suggest that VI is less likely to produce this homogeneous within-cycle performance.

The indication of homogeneity of the response dimensions within the intervals of an FI schedule is in agreement with data reported by Millenson, Hurwitz, and Nixon (1961). Their study concerned response duration. In addition, the results here described for $\int F\, dt$ are paralleled by supplementary data for both F_p and t.

Questions of the generality of the distinction between this aspect of FR and FI performance suggest an area requiring further experimental research. For the present, a few conjectures may be appropriate.

For one thing, a relatively high level of response effort in the interval schedule occurs as soon as responses within the interval commence. This fact suggests that any observed relation between interresponse time (IRT) and response magnitude is coincidental rather than direct. Pausing occurs in both FR and FI, yet in FI the end of the pause does not show a response-effort diminution while in FR it does.

It is possible that the homogeneous effort level found in FI performance relates to the coincidental reinforcement contingencies of such a schedule. A large proportion of the subject's responses are ineffective in the sense that—unlike CRF or FR procedures—they do not alter the probability of reinforcement. During FR, an increase in the vigor of response increases the likelihood that the response will meet the step criterion. As with response frequency, certain variations in performance will result in an increased frequency of reinforcement. The FR schedule may coincidentally provide reinforcement for a chain of responses showing a progressive increase in response vigor. During FI, the minor variations in reinforcement frequency related to variations in the time taken during t^D to reach the reinforcement criterion may not be of discriminable magnitude. Again the parallel with response rate is appropriate. The FI contingency is as likely to provide reinforcement for a single response of criterion magnitude as it is for a progressive chain showing an increase in response vigor.

During FI, the absence of reinforcement (extinction) is most generally attributable to the time when a response occurs rather than to its physical properties. The data indicate that nonreinforcement of a response does not appear to occasion a change in the mode of response in FI. In FR, with the advent of reinforcement critically affected by the physical properties of each response, a nonreinforced response appears to occasion a change in response properties.

Both FR and FI provide situations in which relatively large amounts of time and unreinforced behavior separate successive reinforcements. In addition, an interval schedule provides ample opportunity for the strengthening of nonmeasured behavior (behavior other than response emission). A ratio schedule makes it more likely that control will be gained by measured behavior (response emission). These differences of opportunity may well underscore the observed differences of within-cycle performance. For the present, the FI schedules have provided us with an apparently unique condition in which a sequence of unreinforced responses does not produce a progressive increase in response vigor.

Summary and Conclusions

The performance of rats during FR and FI reinforcement varies with both the schedule requirements and the criteria for response-contingent experimental operations. Changes in force or effort criteria may affect the frequency of responses, and conversely, changes in the interval or ratio requirements may affect the physical properties of the individual responses.

In FR performance, the mean effort of response tends to increase with an increase in the effort requirement (criterion) for either step advances in the ratio count or reinforcement. When the criterion is low, an increase in the ratio length also produces an increase in the effort expenditure of responding. With higher criteria, this effect does not appear. The cumulative effort of response for a complete ratio cycle having high criteria appears to relate directly to the ratio length. With such criteria, the cumulative effort expenditure within a cycle may be accounted for largely in terms of the number of responses emitted. The mean effort for individual responses appears to vary with ratio length only when the criteria are low.

Postreinforcement pauses in responding relate to both the criteria and the ratio length. In general the greater the effort expenditure per reinforcement, the greater the duration of the postreinforcement pause. Nevertheless, the regularity of FR reinforcement appears necessary. High effort expenditures during VR reinforcement do not produce commensurate pause durations. This observation suggests that the effort expenditure serves in a discriminative capacity, since effort expenditure per se does not produce pausing.

Within the ratio cycle there are systematic changes in the response properties. The first responses following reinforcement are generally of a low level of effort. Subsequently, there is a regular increase in effort as the unreinforced sequence progresses. This pattern corresponds to an increasing likelihood that, as reinforcement is approached, responses meeting the criterion will be emitted. This progressive increase occurs both when responses of elevated effort are required to advance the ratio count and also when no elevated step criterion is employed. Nevertheless, the reinforcement criterion at the end of the unreinforced run exerts control over the response properties during the run. When a long unreinforced run is required, but a response of low effort level will produce reinforcement, responses within the ratio cycle are lower in effort than when some higher reinforcement criterion is employed. Although the effort elevation during a ratio cycle may be attributable in part to an extinction phenomenon, the evidence clearly indicates that some measure of control is exerted by the specific criteria for step advances and for reinforcement.

Fixed-interval schedules produce results that are comparable with FR performance in several respects. The total effort expenditure for each reinforcement increases with both interval length and with the reinforcement criterion. In general, it appears that lengthening the interval primarily increases the number of responses emitted, leaving the mean effort for individual responses relatively unaffected. A change in the criterion, on the other hand, produces a commensurate change in the mean effort.

One interesting difference between ratio and interval schedules relates to the performance within the sequence of unreinforced responses of a cycle. On FI schedules, there is no systematic change in the response properties. Initial exposure to a schedule may produce a progressive effort increase during a sequence of unreinforced responses. However, the cycle becomes more homogeneous following a period of exposure to the reinforcement contingencies.

In general, it is apparent that effort of response is a significant variable in operant behavior. When an effort requirement is imposed, there is a general tendency for the performance to be "shaped" to meet this requirement. Effort output itself also appears to serve a discriminative function for subsequent behavior.

Chapter Nine

Sequential Effects
during Fixed-Ratio Reinforcement[1]

A SHARP DISTINCTION between the physical properties of responses under the direct control of reinforcement and those occurring in an extinction context has been a salient feature of the experimental results reported in the foregoing chapters. Progressive regular reinforcement (CRF) has been seen generally to lead subjects to conformity to the reinforcement criterion and to reduction in the variability of performance. Subsequent nonreinforcement has produced a general increase in the vigor of behavior and greater variability.

In addition to the experiments reported here, comparable findings have been reported by several other investigators. Antonitis (1951) measured the physical locus of a nose-poking response in white rats. The variability decreased under CRF and increased during extinction. Margulies (1961) and Millenson and Hurwitz (1961) have also found increases in the variability of response during extinction or during experimental procedures in which lever-press responses go unreinforced. Numerous studies employing a double runway situation have described a comparable increase in the speed of response directly following an unreinforced trial (Amsel, 1958).

In the preceding chapter several behavioral effects, examined during FR performance, were reported. Systematic changes within a schedule cycle were indicated. The present chapter offers a more detailed examination of these response variations. In particular, direct and immediate effects of reinforcement and nonreinforcement are considered. To study these effects, we made certain modifications in FR

[1] A brief report of a portion of the research described in this chapter is found in Mintz, D. E., *Science*, 1962, *138*, 516.

programming. Instead of using the usual single reinforced response for each ratio cycle, we reinforced some of the subjects for two or more successive responses. Consequently, the particular FR is defined both by the number of successive reinforced responses and by the number of successive unreinforced responses that constitute a single complete FR cycle.

The general class of schedule is described as an $FR(N^R)$-N^U schedule, with N^R equivalent to the number of reinforced responses, N^U the number unreinforced. We have indicated N^R by Roman numerals, N^U by Arabic numerals. Therefore, FR(IV)-12 would indicate a 16-response cycle, with the first 4 responses reinforced and 12 subsequent unreinforced responses. Each cycle position may then be conveniently identified by the appropriate ordinal number:

$$\text{I II III IV } 1 \; 2 \; 3 \; 4 \; 5 \; 6 \ldots 12$$

This procedure makes it possible to evaluate progressive reinforcement effects over sequences of several responses. In order to minimize criterion effects, the criteria for both step advances and reinforcement have been kept at the response threshold (2.5-gm. peak force). Of particular interest in the present procedure is the fact that the reinforcement contingency does not directly impose restrictions on any of the response dimensions. So long as the behavioral event is of recordable magnitude (that is, threshold), it produces the immediate response contingency—step advance or reinforcement. In the previous chapter, it was noted that the progressive increase in response vigor during the unreinforced response sequence typically corresponded to an increase in the likelihood of achieving the step or reinforcement criterion. In a sense, the experiment described in this chapter provides a control for such a procedure, since the threshold-level criteria make systematic increases in response vigor inefficacious, or at least, unnecessary.

Since the procedure does not provide a selective differentiation of particular response variants beyond that necessary to attain threshold, systematic changes in the relative strength of different response variations must be related to some coincidental differentiation or to a differentiation that is procedurally independent of selective reinforcement.

Procedure

The experimental design employed three groups of five animals each. All of the animals were initially run for a period of five days under a regular reinforcement regimen, with the 2.5-gm. threshold as the reinforcement criterion. They were given 50 reinforcements per day.

The animals were subsequently run for 12 days on each of three different modified fixed-ratio schedules. During the schedule phases of the study, Group I always received one reinforcement in each fixed-ratio cycle, while Groups II and III were reinforced for two and four successive responses respectively. Six, 12, and 24 unreinforced responses were required, in that order, during the three schedule phases. For instance, during the first schedule phase a complete FR cycle for Group I involved a single reinforced response followed by six unreinforced responses, FR(I)-6; Group II, two successive reinforced responses followed by six unreinforced responses, FR(II)-6; Group III, four successive reinforced responses, followed by six unreinforced responses, FR(IV)-6. Every animal performed 25 FR cycles per day.

Following the schedule phases, two animals from each group were run for four additional days under regular reinforcement. The sequence of experimental procedures is summarized in Table 9-1.

In addition to the 15 animals run under the basic design, one animal was run with FR(VI)-12 (six reinforced responses followed by 12 unreinforced responses) to explore the consequences of this longer rein-

TABLE 9-1

Sequence of Experimental Procedures

Days	Group I	Group II	Group III
5 [1]	CRF	CRF	CRF
12 [2]	FR(I)-6	FR(II)-6	FR(IV)-6
12 [2]	FR(I)-12	FR(II)-12	FR(IV)-12
12 [2]	FR(I)-24	FR(II)-24	FR(IV)-24
4 [3]	CRF	CRF	CRF

[1] 50 reinforcements/day.
[2] 25 cycles/day.
[3] 50 reinforcements/day. Two animals from each group.

forced sequence. The consistency of this animal's performance with that of the others appears to justify the inclusion of data for this one animal.

Results and Discussion

Measures of peak force, duration, and the time integral of force were taken for all responses occurring during the course of the experiment. The interresponse times (IRTs) were measured on a polygraph.

With 25 cycles run for each animal in an experimental session, response samples of $N = 25$ exist for each ordinal position within a cycle as well as a sample of $N = 25(N^R + N^U)$ responses for the animal's entire performance on that day.

Within-Cycle Effects

Peak Force. The systematic variations in peak force that occur in the course of a schedule cycle are shown in Figs. 9-1, 9-2, and 9-3.

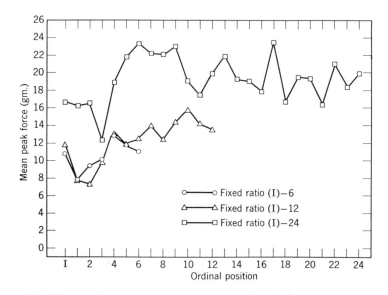

Figure 9-1 Mean peak force of response as a function of ordinal position within a ratio cycle, for fixed ratio (I)-6, fixed ratio (I)-12, and fixed ratio (I)-24. Curves reflect group means. The reinforced response is indicated by the Roman numeral.

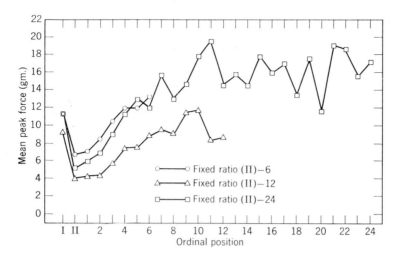

Figure 9-2 Mean peak force of response as a function of ordinal position within a ratio cycle, for fixed ratio (II)-6, fixed ratio (II)-12, and fixed ratio (II)-24. Curves reflect group means. The reinforced responses are indicated by Roman numerals.

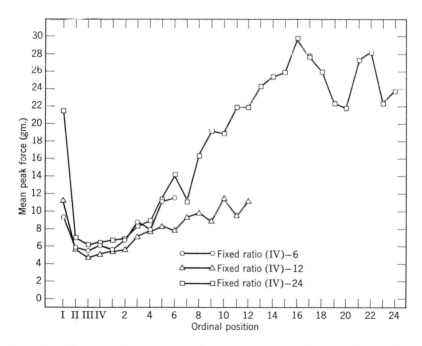

Figure 9-3 Mean peak force of response as a function of ordinal position within a ratio cycle, for fixed ratio (IV)-6, fixed ratio (IV)-12, and fixed ratio (IV)-24. Curves reflect group means. The reinforced responses are indicated by Roman numerals.

Each point represents the mean for the entire group on the last day of each schedule. The functions are characterized by a sharp drop in mean peak force immediately following the initial reinforcement (position I) and a negatively accelerated force increase in the nonreinforced positions. For Group I under FR(I)-24 (Fig. 9-1), the characteristic pattern is less evident; the sharpest drop appears at position 3. Two of the five animals in Group I displayed the typical form of the function, but every animal showed a substantial force drop within the first few cycle positions. At the time of experimentation, it was observed that the animals under FR(I)-24 frequently "overshot" reinforcement, emitting several rapid responses after pellet delivery and prior to tray approach. The delayed force drop appeared to correspond to these occasions.

The curves for peak force as a function of ordinal position in the ratio cycle are shown for four individual animals in Fig. 9-4. The four schedules represented in this figure all contained 12 unreinforced responses per cycle. One, two, four, or six successive responses were reinforced for the different animals, as indicated in the figure.

Duration and the Time Integral of Force of Response. Mean duration and the mean time integral of force of response display the same general form as the peak-force curves. Reinforcement is followed by a sharp drop in each type of measure, and nonreinforcement produces a gradual increase. Figures 9-5, 9-6, and 9-7 show curves for Groups I, II, and III respectively, with time integral of force at the top (*A*) and duration at the bottom (*B*).

Deserving of comment is the relation between levels of peak force, duration, and the time integral of force of response during schedule performance as compared with CRF. During CRF the mean peak force for the entire group was 7.8 gm., the mean duration 0.30 second, and the mean time integral of force 1.4 gram-seconds. Referring these values to Figs. 9-5 through 9-7, it can be seen that there is a considerable reduction in response duration during FR performance. Despite the cyclical variations during the FR cycle, almost every cycle position for every group displays a mean response duration well below the level that was characteristic of the group during CRF, but this reduction is not shown for the peak force or time integral of force of response. Although the levels of these two response measures are comparable with the CRF values for FR cycle positions immediately following reinforcement (Figs. 9-1 through 9-7), at the end of unreinforced runs both the peak force and the time integral of force of re-

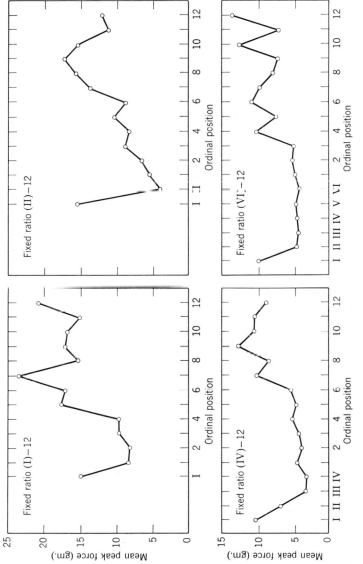

Figure 9-4 Mean peak force of response as a function of ordinal position within a ratio cycle for four individual subjects. Each cycle contained 12 unreinforced responses. The number of reinforced responses varied with subjects and is indicated by the appropriate Roman numerals (after Mintz, 1962).

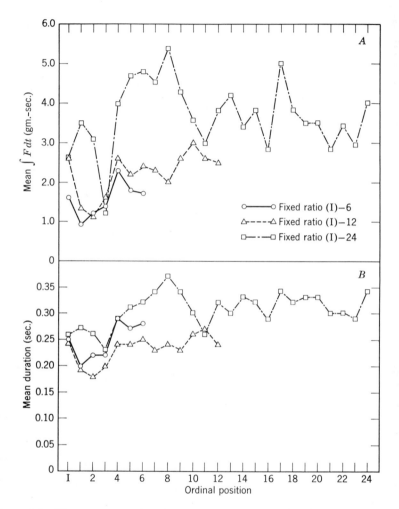

Figure 9-5 Mean response effort (*A*) and mean response duration (*B*) as functions of ordinal position within ratio cycles for fixed ratio (I)-6, fixed ratio (I)-12, and fixed ratio (I)-24. Curves reflect group means.

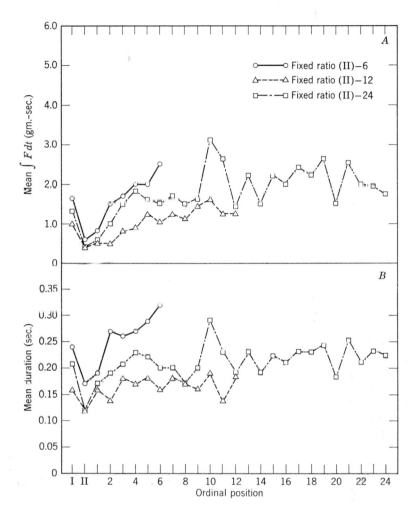

Figure 9-6 Mean response effort (A) and mean response duration (B) as functions of ordinal position within ratio cycles for fixed ratio (II)-6, fixed ratio (II)-12, and fixed ratio (II)-24. Curves reflect group means.

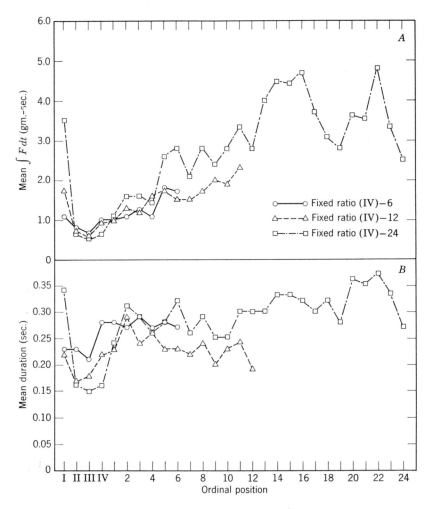

Figure 9-7 Mean response effort (*A*) and mean response duration (*B*) as functions of ordinal positions within ratio cycles for fixed ratio (IV)-6, fixed ratio (IV)-12, and fixed ratio (IV)-24. Curves reflect group means.

sponse are elevated considerably above the average level of CRF. A possible basis for the distinction between response duration and peak force and the time integral of force is discussed later in this chapter.

Ordinal Position Distribution of Peak Force

The differences in mean peak force of response among the ordinal positions are attributable largely to differences in the amount of skewness of the distributions. This is evident in Fig. 9-8 showing the 30th $(X_{.30})$, 50th $(X_{.50})$, 70th $(X_{.70})$ and 90th $(X_{.90})$ percentile values of the distribution of peak force at each ordinal position on the last day of FR(N^R)-6. All three groups in Fig. 9-8 display increasing skewness in the unreinforced cycle positions. This is seen as a sharp rise in the 90th percentile; the medians $(X_{.50})$ are relatively flat across all of the cycle positions. The extinction effect may be described as producing an increased probability of occurrence of high forces.

The curves for Group I (Fig. 9-8, left) pass through a maximum, decreasing in the final unreinforced positions. All three groups show position I somewhat less skewed than position 6, although position I has the maximum number of unreinforced responses preceding it. All of the animals in Group I show this peak force decline in the final unreinforced positions. Hence, for FR(I)-6 at least, the extinction effect does not appear to be a purely monotonic function; a force diminution occurs prior to reinforcement. The phenomenon is also evident in the group curve for mean peak force (Fig. 9-1). This force reduction may possibly reflect a secondary reinforcement effect related to the discrimination of cycle length.

The shape of the distributions is further revealed by a comparison of the means and the standard deviations of the means of peak force. Figures 9-9 and 9-10 show the ordinal-position functions for these two distribution parameters for three animals from Groups II and III under FR(N^R)-24. Each animal shows the typical ordinal-position function with both the mean and the standard deviation. The standard deviations are lower than the means for the positions immediately following reinforcement, while in the nonreinforced positions the means and standard deviations are approximately equal. Several animals show a rapid transition in the relative size of the two parameters. A correlation between the mean and standard deviation is evident, as is typical of skew distributions. However, the ratio of magnitude seems to be related to ordinal position.

No attempt was made to recover performance under the various

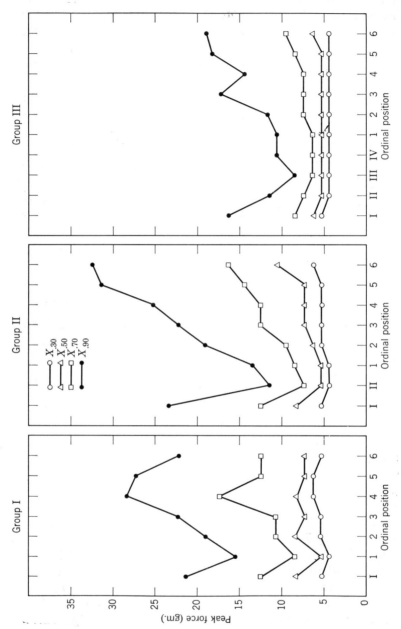

Figure 9-8 Selected percentile values of peak-force distributions for each group under FR (N^R)-6 as a function of ordinal position within a ratio cycle (the reinforced cycle positions are indicated by the Roman numerals).

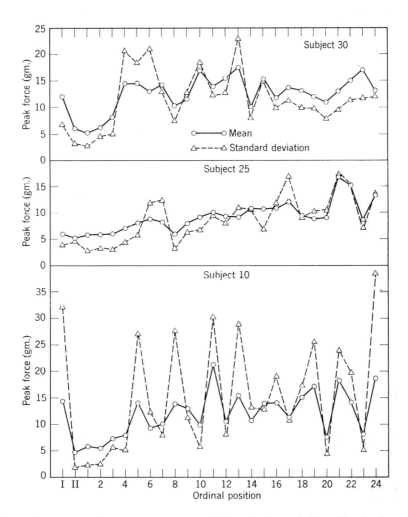

Figure 9-9 The mean and standard deviation of the peak-force distributions as a function of ordinal position within a ratio cycle, fixed ratio (II)-24, subjects 30, 25, and 10.

schedules after exposure to other schedules. Nevertheless, the basic reinforcement and extinction effects were seen in every schedule cycle. The cycle positions reflecting the maximum reinforcement effect typically manifested distributions of peak force comparable to those found during CRF. Table 9-2 presents means and standard deviations of peak force for two animals from each group under CRF (before and after schedule performance) and for position 1 on the last day of each schedule. Position 1 was selected because it follows the greatest

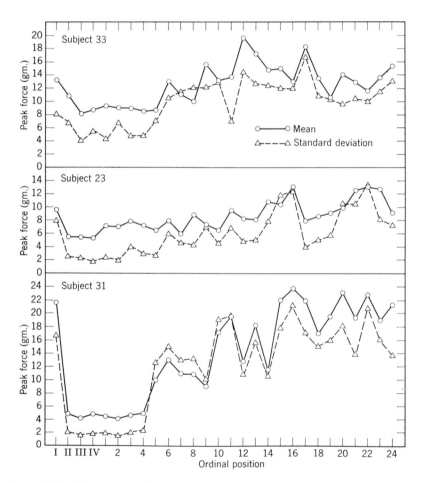

Figure 9-10   The mean and standard deviation of the peak-force distributions as a function of ordinal position within a ratio cycle, fixed ratio (IV)-24, subjects 33, 23, and 31.

TABLE 9-2

*Means and Standard Deviations of Peak Force for CRF and Position 1
in Ratio Cycles*

Peak Force (gm.)

Sessions

Subjects	CRF day 5		FR(NR)-6 position 1		FR(NR)-12 position 1		FR(NR)-24 position 1		CRF 2 day 1	
	$\overline{X}$	S	$\overline{X}$	S	$\overline{X}$	S	$\overline{X}$	S	$\overline{X}$	S
Group I										
22	11.2	5.5	9.2	10.2	4.6	2.9	8.2	7.1	7.4	5.0
34	5.2	3.1	5.6	2.2	7.8	20.7	22.3	40.3	6.1	3.8
Group II										
25	8.7	3.8	9.9	5.5	3.8	2.6	5.8	2.7	4.8	2.5
27	10.4	5.7	6.0	3.0	5.2	3.1	5.0	2.1	6.8	3.1
Group III										
32	10.9	5.0	5.3	1.9	5.4	2.3	6.9	3.1	7.2	2.5
33	9.3	4.8	7.3	3.4	8.0	4.6	9.4	4.4	9.7	4.1

number of antecedent reinforced responses. Position 1 of the FR
schedules frequently shows a lower mean than does CRF. Only for
animal 34, receiving one reinforcement before position 1, was there
substantial increase in the peak force of response at position 1 during
FR performance.

Interresponse Time and Peak Force

The relation between the rate and the peak force of response is
examined for animals 25 and 28. Tables 9-3 and 9-4 show scattergrams
for peak force and interresponse time (IRT) for the two animals under
FR(NR)-12. It is evident that the relations are not linear. In each case
an L-shape is described. The occurrence of a high force after a long
IRT is of negligible probability. Nevertheless, low and high forces
occur with short IRTs, and similarly, low forces occur frequently after
both short and long IRTs. The relation is best described by a bound-
ary precluding instances of high peak force with long IRTs.

Table 9-5 gives the standard deviations of the distributions of peak
force of response and IRT at each cycle position for animals 25 and

28, FR(N^R)-12. Peak force shows the greatest variability in the very cycle positions where IRTs are most stereotypic. Immediately following reinforcement, IRTs are most likely to vary, whereas peak force tends to be low and of uniform magnitude. Rank-order correlation coefficients for the standard deviations of both measures are shown at the bottom of Table 9-5. Each of the negative correlations is significantly different from a chance relation at the 5 per cent level.

Postreinforcement and Extinction Effects

The salient features of this study appear to be summarized in terms of the following two primary effects: a postreinforcement effect, resulting in responses of low force, short duration, low time integral

TABLE 9-3

Frequency Distribution for Peak Force and Interresponse Time
Subject 25 FR(II)-12

Peak Force (gm.)

Interresponse Time (sec.)	0–4.9	5.0–9.9	10.0–14.9	15.0–19.9	20.0–24.9	25.0–29.9	30.0–34.9	35.0–39.9	Over 40
Over 4.80	14	5	2						
4.57–4.80	1								
4.33–4.56	1								
4.09–4.32	3								
3.85–4.08	3	1							
3.61–3.84	2	1							
3.37–3.60	1	1							
3.13–3.36	5								
2.89–3.12	2	1							
2.65–2.88	3	1							
2.41–2.64	3		1				1		
2.17–2.40	7	2			1				
1.93–2.16	2	3	1						
1.69–1.92		3	1						
1.45–1.68	3	1		1					
1.21–1.44	3								
0.97–1.20	2	4		1	1				
0.73–0.96	5	4	3		1	2			
0.49–0.72	11	8	5			1			
0.25–0.48	29	13	4	1		1			
0–0.24	79	57	13	11	6	3	2		

TABLE 9-4

Frequency Distribution for Peak Force and Interresponse Time
Subject 28 FR(IV)-12

Peak Force (gm.)

Interresponse Time (sec.)	0–4.9	5.0–9.9	10.0–14.9	15.0–19.9	20.0–24.9	25.0–29.9	30.0–34.9	35.0–39.9	Over 40
Over 4.80	22	16	1						
4.57–4.80									
4.33–4.56	1	2		1					
4.09–4.32	2	1							
3.85–4.08	1								
3.61–3.84	3								
3.37–3.60	3	2							
3.13 3.36	5	5							
2.89–3.12	8	1							
2.65–2.88	8	3	1						
2.41–2.64	4	2							
2.17–2.40	9	2							
1.93–2.16	6	2						1	
1.69–1.92	3		1						
1.45–1.68	1	1	1			1			
1.21–1.44	3	1	1						
0.97–1.20	8	2	1		1	1			
0.73–0.96	8	5	4			2	1		
0.49–0.72	11	13	5	5	4	1			2
0.25–0.48	20	19	7	7	4	2	1	1	1
0–0.24	42	39	23	6	7	7	8	3	17

of force, and restricted variability; and an extinction effect, producing a progressive elevation in peak force, duration, and the time integral of force. The changes proceed largely from an increasing probability of high values of the response dimensions as extinction proceeds. These general effects were foreshadowed by studies reported in preceding chapters. However, the present study has demonstrated that these effects can run their full course within a single fixed-ratio cycle *and will do so repeatedly*. Systematic variation of the amount of extinction produces peak-force levels that increase directly with the number of unreinforced responses in a cycle. There is also some indication that the peak-force level is inversely related to the length of the reinforced sequence.

The reinforcement effect occurs rapidly; often it is seen after a single

TABLE 9-5

Standard Deviations of Peak Force and Interresponse Time for Successive Cycle Positions

Subject 25			Subject 28		
Ordinal Position	S_{F_P} (gm.)	S_{IRT}(sec.)	Ordinal Position	S_{F_P} (gm.)	S_{IRT}(sec.)
I	5.63	0.60	I	20.42	0.27
II	2.78	8.19	II	2.43	1.38
1	2.56	2.66	III	2.30	1.11
2	1.88	13.99	IV	2.95	9.27
3	3.51	1.67	1	2.41	8.36
4	5.67	11.50	2	5.76	6.38
5	6.89	0.48	3	10.25	10.59
6	7.94	0.66	4	14.49	2.39
7	8.29	0.50	5	11.51	0.21
8	6.49	0.63	6	10.18	0.50
9	6.37	0.21	7	14.36	0.50
10	7.23	0.24	8	20.64	0.36
11	5.08	0.34	9	9.56	0.38
12	5.79	0.39	10	47.75	0.34
			11	19.95	0.55
			12	20.36	0.50

Rank Order Correlation −.67   Rank Order Correlation −.70

reinforced response. Although this study did not attempt to recover the performance of earlier schedules in the sequence of procedures, the recovery of regular reinforcement performance was demonstated by the cyclical nature of performance within single experimental runs. Each cycle can be interpreted as manifesting the basic extinction and reinforcement effects.

The cyclical reinforcement and extinction effects demonstrated for peak force are also characteristic of response duration and the time integral of force. Within any schedule cycle, the measurements of the three dimensions are parallel and correlated. The positive correlation between peak force and response duration, in fact, exists on a response-by-response basis within a single session for a single animal. However, this correlation may reflect nothing more than an inherent physical relation. High forces may simply require longer periods of response emission than low forces. Despite their positive correlation during FR performance, response durations are generally lower than under regular reinforcement, and peak force is higher. Comparable results for response duration have been reported by Schaefer and Steinhorst (1959).

It has been shown that extinction after CRF produces increased response duration (Margulies, 1961; Chapter 3). The present study demonstrates the same result within the sequence of ordinal positions of a ratio cycle. Why is it, then, that a schedule involving considerable extinction produces shorter response durations than those in regular reinforcement? The contingencies of a fixed-ratio schedule suggest an explanation that is comparable with the one proposed by Skinner (1938), Anger (1956), and Ferster and Skinner (1957), among others. The increased probability of reinforcement following short interresponse times (IRTs) also applies to short response durations. The number of responses an organism can emit in a specified interval varies with both response duration and IRT. Responses of long duration simply delay the beginning of the next response in succession or the onset of reinforcement. The topographical response changes that occur in going from CRF to FR schedules are a common laboratory observation. These variations coincide with, and apparently facilitate, brief and rapid responses. It appears possible that two opposing tendencies exist for response duration—the tendency for duration to increase under extinction and the differential reinforcement of short durations intrinsic to the ratio schedule.

Peak force, unlike duration, will not lead to greater frequency or probability of reinforcement on those occasions when its absolute value is low. Despite the correlation of peak force with duration within a session, a contingency tending to reduce durations will not necessarily reduce peak force. Conceptually the change may be understood as a change in the slope of the regression line of peak force on response duration.

Coincidental Reinforcement Contingencies in FR

One consequence of the peak-force elevation within an FR cycle is the frequent reinforcement of high peak-force values. Schoenfeld (1950a) proposed that one property of intermittent reinforcement schedules is the reinforcement of unusual response variants. This suggestion, which would appear to be correct, might be applied to explain, in part, the greater resistance to extinction with longer FRs, as reported by Boren (1961). The longer the ratio, the more likely the reinforcement of varied values of the response.

The frequent reinforcement of high force levels would lead one to expect immediate recurrence of such values, but this did not take place. Although the distribution of peak force of response in the initial reinforced cycle position (position I) is characterized by a high mean and considerable variability, this reinforcement is almost invariably followed by a sharp force decline and a great reduction in variability. In effect, the animals return to a mode of performance characteristic of CRF. It would appear that the reinforcement itself served a discriminative function for producing this behavior. Particularly for the animals receiving more than one reinforcement per cycle, the experimental conditions favor a persistence of this post-reinforcement force decline. For these animals, at least one response at a low force level is reinforced. It is interesting to observe that after extended training only those subjects receiving but one reinforcement per cycle showed any evidence of a reduction in the force decline following reinforcement. These animals were the only ones for which the force decline did not produce reinforcement.

In this context one should recall (Chapter 8) that the postreinforcement decline in effort during ratio performance frequently led to responses that fell below the criterion. Comparably, reinforcement of high-force band responses (Chapter 6) generally was immediately followed by responses of insufficient force (below the band). This evidence requires one to entertain the possibility that a decrease in response vigor following reinforcement is a consequence of the reinforcement operation that is, in part at least, independent of the discriminative aspects of the reinforcement. This possibility appears to be a reality even though there can be no doubt that the animals *do* learn to approximate the response dimensions called for by the reinforcement criterion. Whatever postreinforcement force decline is observed is always related to the previously reinforced performance level: compare the $\int F\, dt$ curves in this and the preceding chapter. The interesting and as yet not fully answered question concerns the immediate and short-term behavioral variations that relate to whether or not immediately antecedent responses were reinforced.

Force Variations as Discriminative Stimuli

The systematic changes within a cycle reflected by the three response dimensions (F_p, t, and $\int F\, dt$) may be considered as behavior-produced correlates of cycle position. These correlates may provide the basis for a variety of the aspects of schedule performance attributed to a discriminative process. In discussing the switching behavior in his two-bar study, Mechner (1958, p. 118) stated:

During a run, the animal possibly could change its way of executing the individual responses on lever *A* gradually until it reaches the topographic variant which constitutes the proper S^D for switching to lever *B*. This S^D could be the tactual, kinesthetic, and visual stimulus compound that results from the execution of that variant of the response.

Ferster and Skinner (1957, p. 40) stated concerning fixed ratio:

(A) *Number as a discriminative stimulus.* Probability of reinforcement is maximal when the number of responses emitted equals the ratio. The probability of response is therefore eventually maximal at that point.

And:

(B) *Number of responses since reinforcement as a condition reinforcer.* As a discriminative stimulus the number of responses emitted at reinforcement is also a reinforcing stimulus.

In order for "number" to exert the control suggested, it must be manifested in some discriminable manner. It is quite possible that "counting" aspects of intermittent reinforcement schedule performance relate to the animal's discrimination of the feedback of its own responses. The studies reported in this and the preceding chapter demonstrate that systematic bases for such a discrimination exist in the peak force, duration, and effort of response.

Chapter Ten

Response Magnitude as a Function of Amount of Reinforcement and Drive Level

ALTHOUGH THE CONCEPT of drive as a goad or specific energizer has lost general acceptance over the years since Cannon's (1912) original work, the notion of drive as a nonspecific energizer or "activator" has come into fairly widespread explanatory usage (Hebb, 1955). Since much of the research that has been offered in support of the "activator" notion has been gathered in the runway situation (for example, Amsel, 1958), and since speed of response is not clearly equivalent to magnitude of response, it seemed worthwhile to examine the effect of variation in drive upon the force with which animals come to press levers. Complementary to the view of drive as an "activator" is that of reinforcement as a "deactivator." Consideration of reinforcement as a compensatory member of a drive-reinforcement loop gives rise to one form or another of drive-reduction model. Assuming that drive operations and reinforcement operations are indeed complementary, and taking the behavior of the organism as an index of the relative consequences of reinforcement upon variation in drive level, one is led to the inference that—other things being equal—an increase in reinforcement should act in the same direction upon behavior as a decrease in drive. While this inference is undoubtedly oversimplified (since other things are usually not equal!), it is an elementary consequence of the assumptions of drive-reduction models. Accordingly, the behavioral effects of variation in both drive level and amount of reinforcement were jointly examined and with the same animals.

Lest there be any doubt about the sense in which we use the terms "drive reduction" and "complementary," we want to make clear that our meaning is more closely allied to Estes' conception of drive than to any other (Estes, 1958). For example, we see the ingestive effects of amount of reinforcement as probably being related to his "satiety" cues. The "complementary" aspects of drive versus reinforcement operations are similar in concept to the inverse relationship he has hypothesized for satiety versus deprivation cues. In short, we would argue that the behaviorally effective consequences of drive and reinforcement operations consist of providing cues for the organism. The reinforcing effect of a pellet of food may be only remotely related to its nutritive value; its influence upon behavior is more discriminative than caloric in character.

The research reported in this chapter should be viewed as but a preliminary step in the direction of a potentially more thorough series of experiments. The only excuse for publishing the sparse data presently available is that they describe phenomena that perhaps are unique and that others may wish to replicate or to extend.

Procedure

With the exception of Phase 2 (extinction), all phases of the experiment involved CRF, 35 reinforced responses per session, at an 8-gm. criterion. As indicated in Table 10-1, three levels of drive and four amounts of reinforcement were examined (five, if one includes extinc-

TABLE 10-1

Experimental Conditions

Phase	Number of Sessions	Drive	Reinforcement
1	20	24 hr.	45 mg.
2	3	24 hr.	none (extinction)
3	6	24 hr.	45 mg.
4	6	24 hr.	20 mg.
5	6	prefed (8 gm.)	20 mg.
6	4	48 hr.	20 mg.
7	11	24 hr.	20 mg.
8	10	24 hr.	2 × 20 mg.
9	5	24 hr.	2 × 45 mg.

tion as a zero amount of reinforcement condition). Although the experiment was begun with six animals, one died during Phase 5; none of this animal's data has been included in the analysis.

Results and Discussion

The consequences of the operations listed in Table 10-1 are shown in Fig. 10-1. The group mean peak force is given as a function of consecutive sessions within each phase. Phases 1, 2, and 3 show the usual effects of acquisition (CRF), extinction, and reconditioning (see Group III, Chapter 3). Of particular interest are the subsequent phases, concerned with variation in either amount of reinforcement or in drive level.

Amount of Reinforcement

Phases 7, 8, and 9 show the effect upon force of response of amount of reinforcement, in that the reinforcement is increased from 20 to 40 to 90 mg., and drive is held constant at 24 hours of deprivation. Note that the Phase 8 condition was obtained by reinforcing the animals with two 20-mg. pellets; the 90-mg. reinforcement (Phase 9) consisted of two 45-mg. pellets. That the effects observed were not the consequence of *size* of pellets per se is indicated by the comparison of Phase 7 with Phase 8; that they were not due to the *numbers* of pellets per se is shown by the comparison of Phase 8 with Phase 9. In the present experiment, number and size of pellets appear to be consequential only insofar as they contribute to the overall amount of reinforcement.

Friedman's Chi-Square Test was used to evaluate the reliability of the differences between performances on the last days of Phases 7, 8, or 9. This nonparametric test indicates that the observed differences may be accepted at the 0.01 level of confidence (two-tailed comparison). Here is some evidence, then, that force of response varies inversely with amount of reinforcement. Additional support for this conclusion was found in observing the animals' behavior when they were exposed to the 20-mg. pellet for the first time (going from Phase 3 to Phase 4). At this point, the amount of reinforcement was decreased, rather than —as in Phases 7, 8, and 9—progressively increased. Yet the effect was in the expected direction—each of the five animals showed an increase in force level.

A further comparison suggests itself: should not extinction be con-

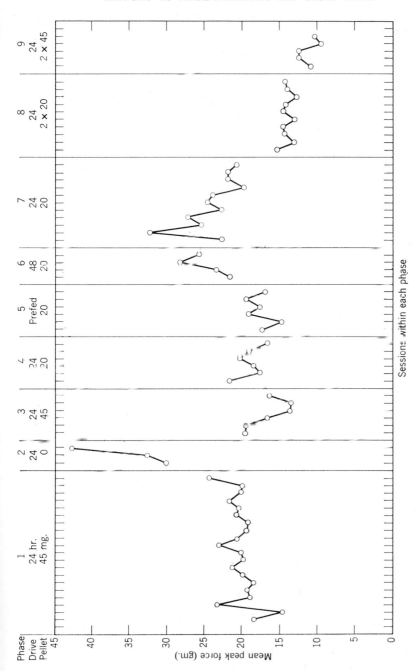

Figure 10-1 Mean peak force of response as a function of successive days during which drive level and amount of reinforcement were systematically varied. Data reflect the group mean. Phase number, drive level, and amount of reinforcement for each phase are noted above the curve. Except for Phase 2, an 8-gm. criterion for regular reinforcement was used.

sidered as a zero point in an amount of reinforcement continuum? And, if it is, should not force level be highest for this value of reinforcement? The answer to this conjecture is already known; extinction *does* produce high forces, the highest shown, in particular, in Fig. 10-1 (Phase 2).

A rough approximation of the functional relation between peak force and amount of reinforcement is given in Fig. 10-2. The values indicated are those of the last sessions of Phase 2 (extinction) as well as of Phases 7, 8, and 9, the last three being selected as the most stable of the phases available. Without attaching too much importance to it, the expression for the curve is:

$$Y = 35e^{-.04x} + 8$$

The "offset" or asymptote represented by "8" is actually an assumed theoretical value and is based on the criterion of 8 gm. in this experiment. The assumption does not seem to do too much violence to the form of the function; the sparse points available seem to be reasonably well fit.

In examining the implications of the general finding that emitted force varies inversely with amount of reinforcement, one must carefully scrutinize the conditions under which these data were obtained. To recapitulate, the animals were all initially exposed to CRF at an 8-gm. criterion, with drive at 24-hour deprivation, and with reinforcement at 45 mg. ("standard" pellet). The consequent variations

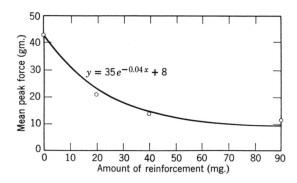

Figure 10-2   Mean peak force of response as a function of amount of reinforcement. A single group of animals was exposed to all the indicated values of reinforcement. An empirically fitted curve and its equation are shown. Regular reinforcement with an 8-gm. peak-force reinforcement criterion was used.

in amount of reinforcement are to be viewed, then, against this earlier conditioning history.

In a sense, the general design of this portion of the experiment is similar to tests of changes in reinforcement reported by Crespi (1942), Zeaman (1949), and Di Lollo (1962). In those experiments, decreases in reinforcement generally resulted in increased running time in a runway. If both increased running time and increased force indicate the sort of deterioration in performance that accompanies extinction, and if extinction is but an end point on a continuum of decreased amounts of reinforcement, then the findings in the present situation are compatible with those reported for the runway. Similarly, the improvement in performance (decrease in force of response to a level more closely approximating the criterion) that accompanies increased amounts of reinforcement has its analog in the decreased running times following increased reinforcement in the runway.

Although the analysis so far has emphasized the possibility that the force versus amount of reinforcement function is a consequence of the shift operation, consideration must also be given to an alternative explanation—that a similar function would have been obtained even if separate groups of animals had been originally conditioned with different amounts of reinforcement. This hypothesis has recently been tested (Di Lollo, Ensminger, and Notterman, 1965) and on the basis of the data obtained cannot be rejected. In this recent experiment, five groups of six animals each were reinforced respectively with 20, 40, 60, 80, or 100 mg. of food. As in the previous study, the criterion was 8-gm. peak force. Acquisition lasted 10 days; then all subjects were shifted to the median amount, 60 mg., for another six days. Figure 10-3 gives the mean peak force and its standard deviation for all groups, averaged for the last two days of acquisition. The probability (two-tailed) of obtaining an ordered replication of the five reinforcement amounts in either the force or standard-deviation function is $\frac{2}{5!}$ ($p < .02$) for each curve. By the last two days of the shift phase, these differences disappeared; all groups leveled out at the force value appropriate to the 60-mg. group. This observation and the feasibility of superimposing the peak-force values shown in Fig. 10-3 upon the curve given in Fig. 10-2 compel us to assume that the force-amount of reinforcement function is inherent in the amount of reinforcement and not peculiarly a shift phenomenon.

At first sight, the finding that force of response varies inversely with amount of reinforcement *during original conditioning* seems to lend support exclusively to an "energization" construct. Subjects obtaining

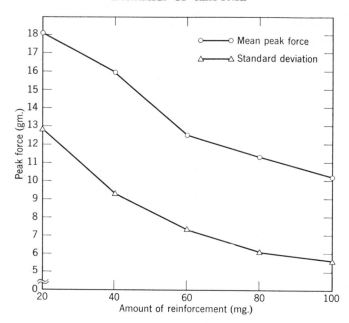

Figure 10-3   Mean peak force of response as a function of amount of reinforcement. A separate group of animals was exposed to each of the indicated values of reinforcement. Regular reinforcement with an 8-gm. peak-force reinforcement criterion was used (after DiLollo, Ensminger, and Notterman, 1965).

lesser amounts of food per response are "innately energized" more than subjects receiving greater amounts. Force emission reflects this activation, and the functions shown in Figs. 10-2 and 10-3 are the consequence. Although this conjecture cannot be denied on the basis of present knowledge, we still lean to the "discriminative" interpretation offered in connection with the earlier study. This explanation is based on the assumption that the major effect of amount of reinforcement is to determine the precision with which the organism comes to approximate the criterion. In other words, the greater the amount of reinforcement, the better the animal learns to make the requisite cutaneous and kinesthetic discriminations. The Di Lollo, Ensminger, and Notterman paper noted: "The hypothesis that amount of reinforcement influences the Ss' ability to discriminate the criterion is in agreement with other results showing a positive relationship between incentive amount and effective discrimination in the *T* maze (Reynolds, 1950; Smith & Duffy, 1957)."

Drive Level

The effect of drive variation may be sought in Fig. 10-1 by comparing the force levels obtained in Phases 5 (prefed), 6 (48-hour deprivation), and 7 (24-hour deprivation). Again, if one takes the last day's performance for each of the phases and applies Friedman's Chi-Square Test, one finds that the forces emitted differ at the 0.04 level of significance (two-tailed test). Force of response tends to increase with increased drive.

In the introduction to this chapter, we remarked that drive and reinforcement, as *experimental* variables, are complementary. Theories and definitions entirely aside, one ordinarily does not attempt to use food as a reinforcer without prior deprivation operations. If one extends consideration of this complementary relationship beyond the mere presence or absence of drive and reinforcement to the relationship between variations in level of drive and in level of reinforcement, one may reasonably make the following inference: once original learning has taken place, and behavior has been stabilized, then an increase in reinforcement should have the same general influence upon performance as a decrease in drive; similarly, a decrease in reinforcement should act in the same direction as an increase in drive. As an extreme example, to illustrate the point, consider the probable subsequent performance of a bar-pressing rat that obtains a 10-gm. ration of food upon making its first response of the session! By the same token, a rat trained to standard 45-mg. pellets momentarily (at least) increases rate of responding upon obtaining a smaller pellet or —for that matter—no pellet at all.

It has already been suggested that extinction should, perhaps, be considered as the ultimate degree of decreased reinforcement. From this viewpoint, it would follow that schedules of fixed or variable ratios of reinforcement, in decreasing the average amount of reinforcement per response, should influence behavior in the same direction as (a) decrease in the amount of reinforcement per se and (b) increase in drive. As indicated in Chapters 8 and 9, the effect of ratio length upon response magnitude is, indeed, in keeping with the foregoing surmise. Lengthening the ratio increases the vigor of the response.

But this reasoning seems to be inadequate in the runway situation. While animals do indeed run faster with increased food deprivation (King, 1959), the Crespi, Zeaman, and Di Lollo data argue that animals run *slower* (rather than faster) with decreased reinforcement. And they run slower even though the random interspersal of totally unreinforced trials among reinforced trials (hence, a decrease in average amount of reinforcement) acts to increase speed of running (Notterman, 1951).

Perhaps the key to the paradox is the extent to which the organism can influence the occurrence of reinforcement by appropriate changes in behavior. In meeting a force criterion, the consequences of pressing with greater or lesser force are quite immediate. In conventional lever-press responding, the animal can modify the time between reinforcements by increasing or decreasing its rate of responding. In the typical runway situation, the absence of a performance criterion and the controlled character of the operant (fixed time between trials) may present special limitations.

These conjectures notwithstanding, the central empirical finding reported in this chapter is that the force of an acquired operant varies directly with changes in hours of deprivation and inversely with changes in amount of reinforcement. The force-drive relationship is certainly consistent with "activation" theories of drive, but other interpretations are also possible. For example, if increased drive is tantamount to decreased reinforcement, and if decreased reinforcement is the genera of which "no reinforcement" (or extinction) is a special member, then the same speculations previously advanced (Chapter 5) to explain extinction-induced increases in force may also be offered to explain drive-induced increases. As we pointed out in Chapter 5, we believe that activation theories tend to be oversimplified in their consideration of discrimination variables and effects. Perhaps we see here again an instance of how our environment establishes reinforcement contingencies and behavioral patterns that superficially resemble respondents but—in the final analysis—are subject to the dynamic laws of the operant. The reader will recognize that in expressing this conjecture we are placing an emphasis upon the cueing function of drive stimuli, much in the same way as has Estes (1958). In addition, we are suggesting that the amount of reinforcement interacts with drive cues in a discriminative manner and influences the facility with which response-induced cutaneous and kinesthetic discriminations are learned.

Chapter Eleven

Proportional Reinforcement

A TYPE OF REINFORCEMENT contingency to be considered now is present in both nature and society but has not—probably for technical reasons—heretofore been studied. It is a contingency in which the organism is reinforced in proportion to the force (loosely, "energy") it emits. The concept seems simple enough, but the experimenters must confess to having predicted results quite different from those actually obtained.

The laboratory prototype is this: an animal receives one pellet for pressing at the criterion, 8 gm.; if it presses just a little harder—say, 2 gm. more—it receives two pellets; and for each additional 2 gm. of force, the subject receives an additional pellet, up to a maximum of five pellets for 16 gm. of force or higher. In Fig. 11-1, representations of both nonproportional (Curve *A*) and proportional reinforcement (*B*) are shown. Curve *A* indicates that the subject receives no reinforcement until it reaches the criterion (8 gm.) and then receives 45 mg. of food (one standard pellet) but no more no matter how hard it presses. Curve *B* indicates that 45 mg. are obtained at 8 gm., 90 mg. (2 pellets) at 10 gm., and so on up to a maximum of 225 mg. (5 pellets) for 16 gm. or higher.

The major experimental question is this: suppose a group of animals, trained in the "conventional" way (according to the contingency represented by Curve *A*), is switched to the reinforcement contingency represented by *B*—would response force go up, down, or remain unchanged? There are two principal considerations.

1. *Selective reinforcement.* Other things being equal, it might be expected that obtaining greater amounts of food for pressing harder should selectively reinforce greater magnitude of response. This "shap-

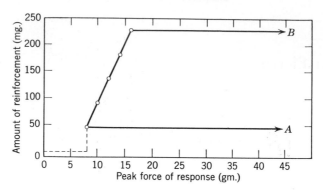

Figure 11-1 The amount of reinforcement given for each reinforced response as a function of the peak force of that response under conditions (A) and (B). (A) depicts a standard 8-gm. reinforcement criterion for which a 45-mg. pellet is given for any response of 8 or more gm. of peak force. (B) depicts an 8-gm. peak-force criterion with an increment of one additional pellet for each additional 2 gm. of peak force, up to a limit of 5 pellets at 16 gm.

ing" would seem to be especially indicated if—as for the prototype cited—the force required to obtain maximum reinforcement is only 16 gm. The advantage to the animal is almost threefold—225 mg. for 16 gm. of force (or a "gain" of 14.1 mg./gm.) compared with 45 mg. for 8 gm. (or 5.6 mg./gm.). Obviously, the comparative energy expenditures involved may also be viewed in terms of distribution proclivities. Given a choice, will a primitive organism press twice at 8 gm. for two successive 45-mg. pellets (5.6 mg./gm.) or once at 10 gm. for the same absolute amount, but at a relative advantage (9.0 mg./gm.)?

2. *Amount of reinforcement.* The foregoing line of reasoning presents a paradox, for—as was shown in Chapter 10—increments in amount of reinforcement tend to *reduce* force of response. Thus, if an animal under proportional reinforcement presses harder and obtains more food, it should—according to this consideration—press *less* hard on the subsequent response.

It is conceivable that both these effects might be operative and that force of response would go up or down as a parametric matter, depending upon the level of drive, the amounts of reinforcements involved, the "gain" of the reinforcement contingency function (the amount of food per unit of required force), and the ability of the organism to discriminate either differential amounts of reinforcement, or differential amounts of force, or both.

Each of the foregoing possibilities entered into the design of the experiment here described, but they did so on a step-by-step basis, as first one procedure was tried, then another, and so on. It seems to us that the exploratory flavor of this research can be best communicated if the entire experiment is reported in a similar step-by-step fashion. Accordingly, we depart in this chapter from our previous format that separated *Procedure* from *Results and Discussion,* and employ, instead, a chronological treatment. For reference purposes, Table 11-1 provides a summary of the conditions characteristic of the successive phases.

Phases of the Proportional-Reinforcement Experiment

Phase 1. The experiment was begun by placing seven rats on CRF, with 8 gm. as the criterion, 50 45-mg. pellets per session as reinforcement, and 24-hour deprivation regimens as drive. A single animal had to be removed from the experiment because of illness. The group mean peak force $(N = 6)$ by sessions of each phase is shown in Fig. 11-2, Part *B*. The curve for Phase 1 (of which only the last three sessions are shown) is comparable with that obtained for Group III in Chapter 3.

TABLE 11-1

Successive Phases, Proportional Reinforcement Experiment

Phase	Increment	Exteroceptive Feedback	Pellet Unit	Drive
1	0	no	45 mg.	24 hr.
2	2 gm.	no	45 mg.	24 hr.
3	4 gm.	no	45 mg.	24 hr.
4	4 gm.	yes	45 mg.	24 hr.
5	4 gm.	yes	20 mg.	24 hr.
6	8 gm.	yes	20 mg.	24 hr.
7	8 gm.	yes	20 mg.	prefed
8 ≅ 6	8 gm.	yes	20 mg.	24 hr.
9	8 gm.	yes	20 mg.	48 hr.
10 ≅ 8 ≅ 6	8 gm.	yes	20 mg.	24 hr.
11	0	yes	20 mg.	24 hr.
12	0	yes	45 mg.	24 hr.
13 ≅ 1	0	no	45 mg.	24 hr.
14	0	0	0	24 hr.

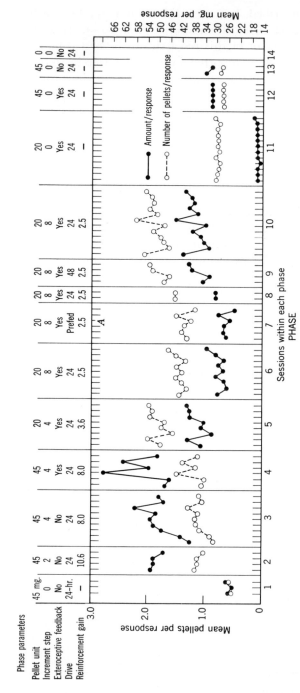

Figure 11-2 Mean milligrams of food and mean number of pellets given per response (*A*) and mean peak force of response (*B*) as a function of successive days under a variety of proportional reinforcement conditions. The parameters of each condition are listed above the curves. They are size of pellets, increment step—the number of grams of peak force above 8.0 required for each additional pellet (0 indicates that proportional reinforcement was not employed), whether or not an exteroceptive feedback stimulus was utilized the food deprivation level, and the "reinforcement gain."

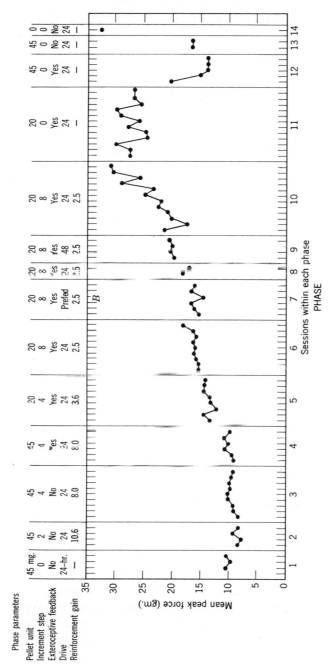

Figure 11-2 Continued.

Phase 2. Beginning with the first session of Phase 2, the subjects were placed on a proportional-reinforcement contingency schedule. Once above the criterion, an animal received an additional pellet for each 2-gm. increment in force up to a maximum of 5 pellets for 16 gm. The pellets were delivered in rapid successive order (separated temporally by 0.01 second) upon conclusion of the response, that is, when the force applied fell below threshold.

The immediate effect of the switch from nonproportional to proportional reinforcement may be seen in Fig. 11-2-*B*; there was a drop in peak force emission that was maintained over the four sessions of Phase 2. This drop was reliable; all six subjects showed it. Accompanying this decrease in force was a decrease in number of responses required to obtain the daily ration of 50 pellets. The decrease was from a mean of 87.7 for the last three days of Phase 1 to a mean of 43.8 for the four days of Phase 2. At first sight, the drop in force and the drop in number of responses seem to be incompatible. If the animals had pressed harder, then a drop in number of responses would have seemed appropriate, since a fixed number of pellets (50) was available, and by pressing harder the animals would have obtained this quantity with fewer responses. But if we examine the force distributions shown in Fig. 11-3, we find that an explanation suggests itself. The subjects emitted approximately 40 per cent of their responses at 10 gm. or better during the last session of CRF. Consequently, when these subjects were shifted to proportional reinforcement, they needed only to maintain this level of responding and receive more than one pellet per response on about 40 per cent of their responses. Actually, as the distributions indicate, the subjects—apparently as a consequence of the increased average amount of reinforcement per response—shifted downward in response magnitude and stabilized at a point where only approximately 30 per cent of their responses received multiple reinforcement.

In short, the Phase 1–Phase 2 comparison leads to the tentative conclusion that, at least for the parametric conditions present, proportional reinforcement simply transforms to greater amounts of reinforcement *for the same response forces,* and that this, in turn, makes for decreased response magnitude. This line of reasoning leads to a generalization—the operation of shifting from regular to proportional reinforcement can only result in greater average amounts of reinforcement (provided the same initial criterion is maintained), and, consequently, decreased response magnitude. This generalization, of course, ignores one of the two principal considerations mentioned earlier—

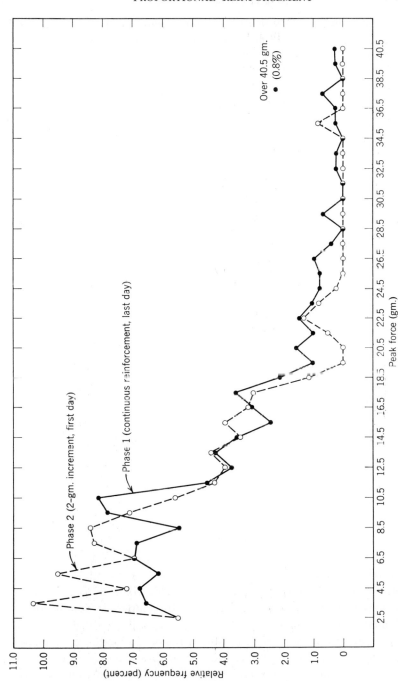

Figure 11-3 Relative frequency distributions of peak force of response for group during Phase 1, regular reinforcement with an 8-gm. peak-force criterion, and Phase 2, proportional reinforcement with an incremental step of 2 gm.

the possible influence of selective reinforcement. Perhaps selective reinforcement in the sense of greater force emission for greater amounts of food can take place, but it did not in the Phase 1–Phase 2 shift simply because the step required for additional pellets was so small (2 gm.) that the animals could not make the necessary difference discrimination. In other words, the upward shaping of response force did not take place because the subjects could not adequately discriminate 8-gm. pressure from 10-gm. or 12-gm. pressure; differential sensory cues were not available, even though differential reinforcement was. As far as the organism was concerned, the procedure may have reduced itself to occasional provision of greater amounts of reinforcement for the same behavior, and, as suggested in Chapter 10, the animal simply learned better to discriminate the criterion. Accordingly, the next phase was undertaken.

Phase 3. In this phase, the force incremental step necessary to obtain additional pellets was changed from 2 gm. to 4 gm. Thus, presumably the greater difference between self-generated pressure cues associated with 8-gm. force and one pellet and the cues associated with 12-gm. and two pellets (and so on) should enhance discrimination of and consequent selective reinforcement for higher force emission.

Examination of Fig. 11-2 does, indeed, indicate a trend upward in force emission. Five of the six animals were higher in response magnitude on session 9 than on session 1, the single inversion being rather slight, 0.4 gm.

This force increase would seem to argue that selective reinforcement for more vigorous responding had taken place, but, again, the amount of reinforcement variable appears to provide a more parsimonious explanation. Note in Fig. 11-2-*A* that the consequence of increasing the incremental step from 2 gm. to 4 gm. is immediate reduction of the amount of reinforcement earned per response in comparison with the last session of Phase 2. It may well be that the observed increase in force stems from this decrease in reinforcement and may be attributed to the "extinction effects" discussed in Chapter 5. The distributions for sessions 1 and 9 of Phase 3 are shown in Fig. 11-4; the observed slight shift to the high side for session 9 is, however, compatible with either selective-reinforcement or amount-of-reinforcement explanations.

To recapitulate by way of providing a rationale for the next phase, the experiment up to this point yields the following information:

1. In going from nonproportional (Phase 1) to proportional (Phase

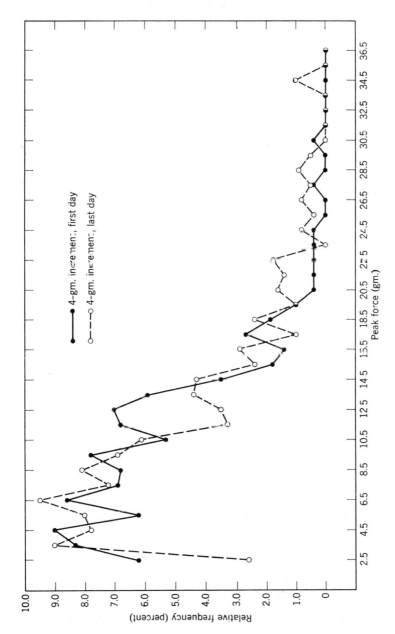

Figure 11-4 Relative frequency distributions of peak force of response for group on first day and last day of Phase 3, proportional reinforcement with an incremental step of 4 gm.

2) reinforcement, either of two changes in performance could have taken place. The animals could have increased magnitude of response, and—if they had—it would have been inferred that selective reinforcement of vigorous responding had taken place. Or, a decrease in response magnitude could have occurred, leading to an interpretation based on the previously established effects of increased amount of reinforcement (Chapter 10). The decrease that was observed may provide the basis for a tentative generalization—that a shift in reinforcement contingencies from nonproportional to proportional reinforcement is accompanied by a decrease in response magnitude, when other parameters are held constant.

2. One serious limitation to this generalization lies in the problem of organism discrimination of the forces involved in the shift from one amount of reinforcement to the next higher amount. Accordingly, in Phase 3 the force incremental step was increased from 2 gm. to 4 gm. The confounding aspect of this approach was the ambivalence of interpretation suggested by the consequent increase in force—interpretation predicated on either decreased reinforcement or enhanced discrimination. Even as changing from nonreinforcement to proportional reinforcement would appear inevitably to lead to *increased* amounts of reinforcement per response followed by decreased response magnitude (at least as an immediate, if transient, consequence of the shift), so increasing the force incremental step would seem invariably to lead to *decreased* amounts of reinforcement per response followed by increased response force.

Then how is one to increase the likelihood of successful discrimination of force magnitudes, thus, in turn, enhancing the possibility of selective reinforcement for higher forces (if, indeed, this does take place)? The solution that suggested itself was undertaken in Phase 4.

Phase 4. A tone oscillator was wired into the system so as to provide an approximately 50-millisecond, 1000 cycles-per-second, 30-decibel sound-pressure-level signal each time the lever was pressed with sufficient force to pass through the criterion and for each successive incremental step above. Thus, a rat pressing the bar with 9 gm. of force would—as the 8-gm. criterion was passed—receive one "beep." If the rat pressed with 13 gm. of force, it would receive a "beep" at 8 gm. and another at 12 gm. For 24 gm. or higher, the rat would procure five signals, one each as its pressure passed through 8, 12, 16, 20, and 24 gm.

The obvious intent of the experimenters was to provide exteroceptive support for the differential pressure cues that would result from application of varying magnitudes of force. This, in turn, would—it was hoped—increase the likelihood of selective reinforcement of higher force magnitudes, without the obfuscating problems of trying to do it by increasing the required incremental step, as in Phase 3.

The results of Phase 4, as summarized in Fig. 11-2-*B,* indicate that the exteroceptive signal did not influence the performance. For the moment, we must leave unanswered the question of whether the tone actually came to act as a cue. Suffice it to say that a cue-removal phase was administered, but much later in the experiment. Because of this planned check on the efficacy of the tone as a cue or secondary reinforcer, the intervening phases included as a regular parameter the same tone-force-level relationship that has been described.

Phase 5. It will be recalled that from Phase 2 to Phase 3 the force incremental step was increased from 2 gm. to 4 gm. Given the distribution of Phase 2 (Fig. 11-3), the change to the 4 gm. incremental step effectively reduced the amount of reinforcement per response (Fig. 11-2-*A*). The animals pressed harder, thereby increasing the amount of reinforcement per response, until (as may be noted in Fig. 11-2-*A*) the amount received was approximately the same as for Phase 2. Was this a coincidence, or would any experimental operation that effectively reduced amount of reinforcement meet with the compensation of more vigorous bar-pressing until a level of approximately 50 mg. per response was reached? We elected to test this possibility in the following two ways: by further increasing the incremental step required for additional pellets (Phase 6); by using 20-mg. rather than 45-mg. pellets as the unit of reinforcement (present phase).

Figure 11-2 shows that from the last day of Phase 4 to the first day of Phase 5 the amount of reinforcement decreased by about 15 mg. (from approximately 51 mg. to 36 mg.). This 30 per cent drop occurred despite the observed increase in response force and despite the shift in number of pellets received per response from a mean of about one to a mean of about two. Figure 11-5 is interesting in that it depicts for the first session of Phase 5 an apparently bimodal distribution of response forces, with one peak below criterion and the other decidedly above. The last session of this phase, shown in Fig. 11-6, may reveal the effects of successive sessions at the new unit of reinforcement in that the below-criterion peak seems to have disappeared. Notwithstanding the marked increase in force level shown by each of the six animals, the amount of reinforcement received did not ever

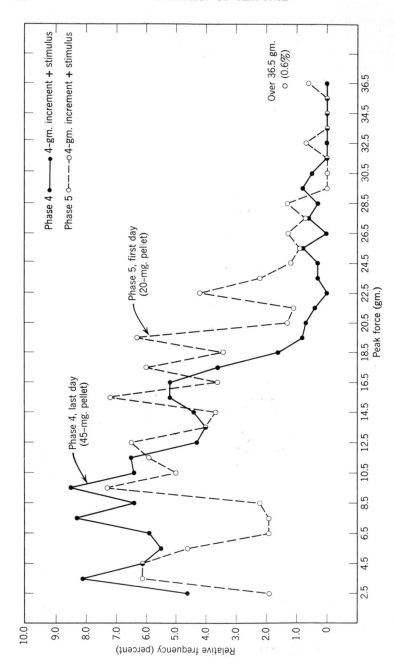

Figure 11-5 Relative frequency distributions of peak force of response for Phase 4 and Phase 5. The conditions vary only in the size of the pellets used.

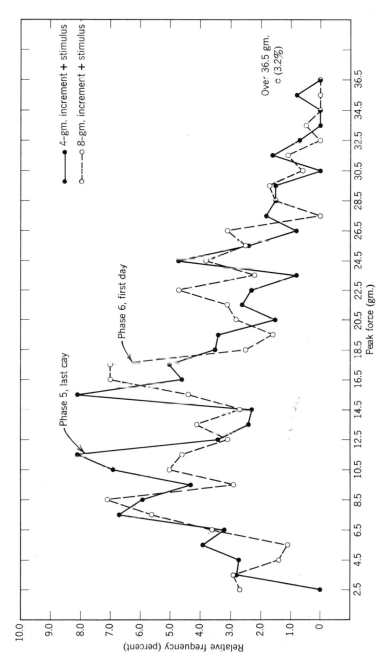

Figure 11-6 Relative frequency distributions of peak force of response for group on the final day of Phase 5 and the first day of Phase 6. The conditions differ only in the size of the incremental step used.

rise to the 50-mg. level prevailing prior to the change in pellet unit; this level would have required a mean of 2.5 pellets per response. Moreover, there is no significant change in amount of reinforcement earned as a function of sessions within Phase 5.

The extent to which the subjects compensated for the decrease in unit of reinforcement is revealed by some simple arithmetic. On the last day before the shift, the animals were averaging 1.14 pellets per response, or 51 mg. (1.14 × 45 mg.). If the same number of pellets per response were obtained in the first session after the shift, the group would have received an average of 23 mg. per response. By pressing harder, however, the animals increased the number of pellets per response to 1.82, yielding 36 mg. Although an increase of 13 mg. does not seem very large, it represents—in relative terms—a 56 per cent increment, with 23 mg. as a base. If the animals had obtained 1.82 pellets per response in Phase 4, their amount of reinforcement would have been 1.82 × 45 mg. or 82 mg. per response.

We may draw the following conclusions: (1) the consequence of reducing the pellet unit is to increase force of responding; (2) the increase is not sufficient to restore the amount of reinforcement obtained to levels prevailing prior to the change in pellet unit, *even though the response force required to achieve complete compensation is well within the animals' repertoire* (compare with the later phases of this experiment and with Chapter 3). The intriguing question of whether there is some generalization to describe and predict the level of force that actually will be emitted under various "gain factors" of proportional reinforcement is put off for the time being.

Phase 6. In Phase 6 we further effectively decreased the amount of reinforcement per response through the expedient of increasing the force incremental step from 4 gm. to 8 gm. Thus, the animals received one 20-mg. pellet at 8 gm. of peak force, two at 16 gm., and so on for a maximum of five pellets (or 100 mg.) at 40 gm. of peak force or higher.

On the last day of Phase 5 the subjects were pressing with sufficient force (between 12.0 and 15.9 gm.) to receive an average of about two pellets or approximately 40 mg. per response. To attain 40 mg. per response in Phase 6, the animals would have had to press, on the average, between 16.0 to 19.9 gm. Actually, they came to press with a mean of 15.7 for session 1, and gradually increased this to 18.4 by the last session. The average amount of reinforcement similarly increased from 30 to 34 mg. Since the increment in food as a function of force proceeds in steps, rather than being continuously proportional with force, one cannot proceed from "force level" to "food obtained" merely on the basis of multiplying by a constant or by interpolation. The value of "amount of reinforcement per response" is computed by dividing 50 pellets times pellet unit (in milligrams) by the number of responses required to obtain the 50 pellets per session. Five out of six animals pressed harder during the last session of this phase than during the first; the relevant group mean distributions are shown in Fig. 11-6 and Fig. 11-7.

With Phase 6, then, as with Phase 5, we see a change in behavior, that is, more vigorous responding; the consequence was that the animals obtained more food than they would have if they had not pressed harder, but still not as much as they had under conditions of the prior phase. If the 14.2-gm. force level of the last day of Phase 5 had been maintained in Phase 6, the average number of pellets each received would have dropped from 2.0 to 1.0. Instead, the animals pressed hard enough to obtain 1.50 pellets per response on day 1 of Phase 6 and gradually increased this to 1.69 by the last day.

Phases 7, 8, and 9. These stages of the experiment were concerned with drive operations. In Phase 7, the animals were prefed for one hour prior to entry into the Skinner box; in Phase 8 the subjects were restored to 24-hour deprivation, and in Phase 9 the animals' runs took place after 48 hours without food. Except for the drive differences in Phases 7 and 9, these three stages were identical with Phase 6, with the 8-gm. criterion, 8-gm. incremental step, 20-mg. reinforcement unit, and tone signals that accompanied each advance through a step or accretion of another pellet.

The results of the drive operations were fully in accord with those described in Chapter 10. In the prefed condition, there was a tendency for the animals to press less hard (see Fig. 11-2-*B* and Fig. 11-7, which compare the distribution of the last session of Phase 6 with that of the first session of Phase 7). Phase 8 shows a slight elevation in force, restoring the animals to the levels of Phase 6, the customary 24-hour drive condition. In Phase 9, the increase of deprivation to 48 hours is characterized by an increase in response magnitude. If the mean peak force for each phase (that is, across all sessions within each phase) is computed for individual animals, then the effect of the drive operation in going from Phase 7 to 8 to 9 is significant at the 0.04 level (Friedman's Nonparametric Chi-Square Test, two-tailed comparison).

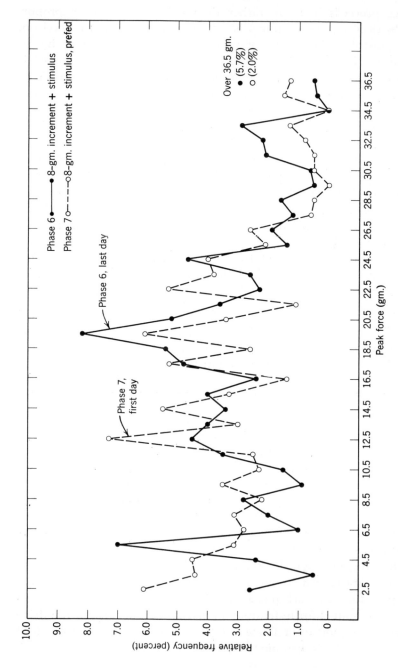

Figure 11-7 Relative frequency distributions of peak force of response for group on the final day of Phase 6 and the first day of Phase 7. The conditions differ only in deprivation level; Phase 7 involves a prefeeding.

Phase 10. Upon completing Phase 9, we restored the animals to 24-hour deprivation, maintaining the same force-reinforcement contingencies. Phase 10, then, was identical in all respects with Phases 6 and 8. Despite this, the curve in Fig. 11-2-*B* depicts not a return to the levels of Phases 6 and 8 but rather a consistent increase in force as a function of sessions. The curve, however, is misleading, inasmuch as the effect shown is not characteristic of the entire group but only of two animals. The group as a whole was not significantly higher on the last day of this phase than it was on the first day. Moreover, in comparing response magnitudes on the last day of this phase with that of the last day of Phase 8 (also 24-hour deprivation) we likewise find no significant change.

Why the two animals responsible for the upward trend in the curve should have shown such striking increases in peak force (one from 17.9 to 39.1 gm. and the other from 23.0 to 64.5 gm.) is difficult to assess. Are these figures indicative of a marginal trend in the direction of selective reinforcement for more vigorous responding? In support of this interpretation is the increase (despite lack of statistical reliability of differences between phases) in the median peak force for the last day of this phase over that for the last day of the previous phase (25 versus 21) and over the last day of Phase 8 (25 versus 17). It is possible, therefore, to argue from the increase in force of response during the previous (48-hour deprivation) phase, that the animals began to learn that pressing harder resulted in more pellets, and that this learning continued into Phase 10. It is at least equally reasonable, on the other hand, to argue that the absence of statistical reliability precludes such an interpretation. The data of this phase remain ambiguous.

Phase 11. In this stage of the experiment we attempted to determine the effects of reverting to nonproportional reinforcement. The criterion was maintained at 8 gm. and the pellet unit at 20 mg. As a consequence, the average amount of reinforcement obtained fell from 41 mg. per response on the last day of Phase 10 to 16 mg. per response on the first day of Phase 11. Based on prior evidence, it would be expected that such a decrease in reinforcement would lead to more vigorous responding, but no such significant change took place. As Fig. 11-2-*B* indicates, the animals remained during this entire phase at approximately the level of the last few sessions of Phase 10.

Our guess was that the subjects had collectively about reached their maximum force level (without special shaping) by the end of Phase 10, and that for this reason the decrease in reinforcement characteristic of the return to nonproportional reinforcement contingencies had no effect. The following two ways suggested themselves for testing this interpretation: placing the rats into complete extinction and comparing the force levels generated during zero reinforcement with those characteristic of the present phase (as was eventually done in Phase 14); increasing the amount of reinforcement, but again in the nonproportional mode, to see whether—as should happen if amount of reinforcement were still effective as a variable—the force level dropped. The latter test was made in the succeeding phase.

Phase 12. Conditions were the same as for Phase 11, except that the pellet unit was changed from 20 mg. to 45 mg. The amount of reinforcement obtained per response rose from 17 to 32 mg. (last day Phase 11 compared with first day Phase 12). For the same sessions, the mean response magnitude fell from 26.9 gm. to 20.2; the decrease was shown by all six animals. By the last session of Phase 12, the mean peak force of response fell further to 13.6 gm. The effect of increasing amount of reinforcement was in the expected direction.

Phase 13. In this phase of the experiment we sought to determine whether the exteroceptive signal introduced in Phase 4 had come to exercise any discriminative control over the force of response.

Even though proportional reinforcement had been discontinued in Phase 11, the animals still received a "beep" upon passing through the criterion. If the subjects had come to depend in some measure upon this auditory cue, it would be expected that they would tend to overshoot their previous force level should the tone signal suddenly be eliminated. This prediction assumed that the exertion of force without the signal had come to be a cue for greater force exertion.

The tone was discontinued beginning with the first session of this phase. Each of the six animals thereupon showed an increase in response force (Fig. 11-2-*B*). By the second session, however, only four of the six animals continued a response force higher than for the last session in which the tone was presented (day 5, Phase 12).

It would appear, therefore, that the exteroceptive signal had indeed contributed to the discriminative control of force emission, and in much the same manner as described in Chapter 7.

Phase 14. The last stage of the experiment consisted of extinction. All six animals rose to such high force levels that their combined mean was the highest of all previous sessions—note single point in graph section for Phase 14. It will be recalled that the data of Phase 11 suggested that the animals were responding then at levels comparable with extinction. That this supposition is probably correct is indicated by the similarity of the levels characteristic of the extinction session; although higher, these magnitudes were not significantly different from those of the last session of Phase 11. Four of the six animals were, indeed, higher during extinction; the two exceptions were the two subjects that were responsible for the positive slope characterizing the session-by-session data of Phase 11.

General Discussion

The unique aspect of proportional reinforcement is that the experimenter determines what we have called the "gain" of the system, but the subject determines through its own behavior the actual amount of reinforcement obtained per response.

With the possible exception of the ambiguous data of Phase 10, the data seem to make it fairly clear that the laboratory rat (perhaps unlike the middle-class American!) does not "work harder to get more." The most striking evidence to support this conclusion was seen in the change in behavior accompanying the transition from Phase 1 (nonproportional) to Phase 2 (proportional); it will be recalled that each animal showed a drop in magnitude of response. That the animals were physically capable of pressing hard enough to have obtained the maximum number of pellets in Phase 2 (16 gm. of force for five 45-mg. pellets) was obvious because the same subjects were pressing with approximately 27 gm. of force at the end of Phase 11 (nonproportional; 8-gm. criterion for one 20-mg. pellet). The latter force value is approximately three times the magnitude of the mean peak force actually emitted in Phase 2.

When the "gain" of the system was decreased from that of Phase 2, either by an increase in the incremental step (Phase 3 and Phase 6) or by a decrease in the unit of reinforcement (Phase 5), the average force of response increased. Now, it could have increased to a level sufficient to obtain the same amount of reinforcement as was "earned" in Phase 2, but it did not. For example, if the subjects had pressed as hard in Phase 3 as they later came to press in Phase 11, they would easily have equaled (and, indeed, greatly exceeded) the amount of reinforcement obtained in Phase 2. Figure 11-8 depicts the

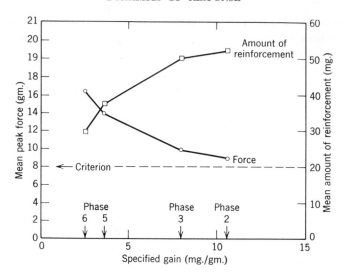

Figure 11-8   Mean peak force of response and mean amount of reinforcement per response as a function of the specified reinforcement gain (the ratio of milligrams of reinforcement available per emitted gram of peak force under the particular experimental condition). The phase of the experiment in which each of the specified gains was employed is indicated along the abscissa.

force levels for Phases 2, 3, 5, and 6 as a function of gain and also indicates the average amount of reinforcement received per response. Note that as gain is decreased (Phase 2, which appeared first, is on the right) force of response increases, but not enough to keep the amount of reinforcement received per response equal to that of Phase 2.[1]

It is also worth noting that for the largest *specified* gain value (10.6 for Phase 2), the animals operate on an *actual* gain of 5.9 mg./gm. (mean amount of 52.3 mg. per response, mean peak force of 8.9 gm.) or only 56 per cent of what they might do. But as specified gain is decreased, the animals tend to become more "efficient," as shown in Fig. 11-9.

[1] The "Specified Gain" was computed for each phase as follows: the amount of reinforcement received at the criterion was divided by the criterion force to yield the gain at criterion (in Phase 2, for example, 45 mg. divided by 8 equals 5.6 mg./gm.); the amount received at the next step was divided by the force required (in Phase 2, 90 mg. for 10 gm. equals 9.0 mg./gm.), and so on, for each of the gains at each of the five reinforcement steps; the resulting "step gains" were then averaged to give the "Specified Gain" (in Phase 2 [5.6 + 9.0 + 11.3 + 12.9 + 14.1]/5 = 10.6).

In short, it appears that even though the emitted force levels generated as a function of decreased gain are not sufficient to keep amount of reinforcement equal to that obtained at the largest specified gain value, and that this discrepancy increases with decreased specified gain (Fig. 11-8), the actual gain values more closely approximate the specified gain limits established by the experimenter, as shown in Fig. 11-9. The latter discrepancy *decreases* with decreased specified gain.

This observation would seem reasonable. One would expect the behavior of biological organisms to be governed not only by amount of reinforcement but also by the energy expended in obtaining the "payoff." Otherwise the phenomenon of selective reinforcement might have operated so as to maximize the magnitude of response and the magnitude of reinforcement. The consequences of proportional reinforcement do not reveal such behavior. Instead, in the interplay between available amount of reinforcement and force required to obtain it, the organism appears to optimize neither of these but rather the quantity that we have called "actual gain." Consequently, "least effort," "selective reinforcement," and "amount of reinforcement" may

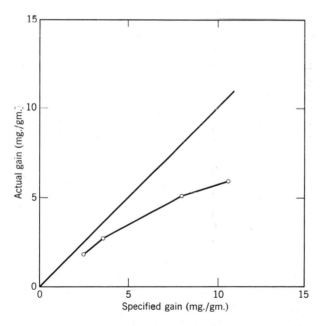

Figure 11-9 Actual gain as a function of specified gain. The straight line of unit slope indicates the upper limit possible for actual gain.

not by themselves sufficiently describe behavior, especially when the natural or experimental environment provides for some consistent relationship between required expenditure of energy and obtained amount of reinforcement. One can only speculate here that the phenomenon depicted in Fig. 11-9 may, at least plausibly, account for the phenomenon shown in Fig. 11-8. To the question implicit in Fig. 11-8—why the animals do not press hard enough to restore to the level obtained in Phase 2 the amount of reinforcement "earned" during the subsequent phases—Fig. 11-9 implicitly answers that it is not behaviorally economical for them to do so, at least for Phases 5 and 6. Proportional reinforcement yields the animal more reinforcement per response only at the expense of greater expenditure of energy; and, indeed, we have observed that when specified gain is decreased, the animal presses harder. But as the actual gain approaches the specified gain, there is less biologically economic advantage in pressing still more vigorously, since greater amounts of food *per gram of force expended* are not increased (see Fig. 11-1).

But this leaves unanswered an even prior question. During Phases 2 and 3, why should the subjects not have pressed hard enough to obtain the maximum number of pellets per response? Why should they not have performed so as to produce actual gain more closely equivalent to specified gain? Phase 11 of the experiment clearly indicates that the force required to obtain maximum reinforcement in Phases 2 and 3 was well within the physical capabilities of the animals. This observation suggests that there are two possible aspects to the economics of the proportional reinforcement situation. The first was described in the previous paragraph—as actual gain approaches specified gain (Phases 5 and 6), there is no further advantage in pressing harder for more food. The second is that regardless of how high the experimenter sets the specified gain (that is, how easy it is for the animal to procure the food), there is a related upper limit to the actual gain that an organism will generate in a free-operant situation. This assumed upper limit may well depend on several variables. Among them would be the following: the absolute amount of reinforcement obtained, as it influences existing drive cues (see Chapter 10); the exertion required to obtain this amount (gain), perhaps as it relates to the ever-present option of pressing again rather than harder; and the capacity of the organism to detect changes in drive cues and in motor feedback cues.

Notice that what has been described is not an argument concerning "least effort." Instead, the speculation concerns another variable:

"amount of reinforcement per unit of force." We also assume that should such a variable be operative, it certainly would be under the influence of previously established reinforcement contingencies.

Despite these qualifications, the potency of "gain" in shaping behavior instead of absolute amounts of reinforcement per response or absolute amounts of expended energy per response is sufficiently conjectural for us to offer it for the present only as a working construct.

Chapter Twelve

Avoidance

THE USE OF AVERSIVE stimuli has found wide application in operant conditioning procedures. In this chapter some of the response properties of behavior maintained with an aversive stimulus (electric shock) are examined. The experimental procedure employs two levels of shock. Additionally, the differences between responding maintained by positive and by negative reinforcement are considered.

This study utilizes a technique described by Sidman (1953a, 1953b). The technique maintains behavior under an avoidance contingency in which each response postpones the onset of a brief aversive electric shock. In the absence of response, the shock recurs with a regular frequency. Two temporal parameters of the schedule are specified. The response-shock interval $(R-S)$ is the period of time each response delays the next shock. The time between successive shocks (when no response intervenes) is termed the shock-shock interval $(S-S)$. Schedules of this sort are typically run with no exteroceptive warning signal to indicate the advent of shock.

According to Skinner (1938) behavior may be maintained when it produces positive reinforcement or removes negative reinforcement. An avoidance schedule provides neither of these conditions directly or obviously as a consequence of individual responses. Explanations of the "reinforcement" for an avoidance response have contained the suggestion that the appropriate control has been assumed by formerly neutral stimuli through some conditioning procedure. Reinforcement for individual avoidance responses is then explained as escape from secondary negative reinforcement (Schoenfeld, 1950b) or "fear reduction" (Mowrer, 1939). Extensive experimental support for these similar theoretical positions has been produced (Kimble, 1961, p. 266),

236

and the role of "fear" in avoidance behavior has undergone extensive analysis (Miller, 1951; Mowrer, 1960). The assessment of avoidance behavior in terms of some escape paradigm is particularly convincing for situations in which a warning signal precedes the aversive stimulus.

In the absence of a warning signal (that is, in a schedule similar to Sidman's) avoidance still occurs. The explanation proposed by Sidman (1953a, 1953b) follows the argument developed by Schoenfeld (1950b). Certain aspects of the organism's own behavior (except for the avoidance response) acquire aversive properties through correlation with shock. The consequence of the correlation is suppression of behavior other than the avoidance response. Escape from the acquired aversive properties of this nonavoidance behavior is possible through emission of the avoidance response. In a sense, the animal generates its own warning signal and subsequently removes it by emitting the avoidance response. A more recent explanation has been proposed by Anger suggesting that Sidman-avoidance may be based on conditioned aversive temporal stimuli (1963). Although Anger's position differs from the earlier explanation in terms of the identity of the stimuli controlling the avoidance response, his proposition is still fundamentally based on an escape paradigm, with the avoidance response maintained through escape from conditioned aversive stimuli.

In the Sidman schedule both the $S-S$ and $R-S$ intervals contribute to the frequency with which shock will occur. However, short $R-S$ intervals will also permit close temporal proximity between the aversive stimulus and the response to be conditioned. Sidman has demonstrated that for a given $S-S$ interval there is generally an optimum $R-S$ interval (Sidman, 1953a). $R-S$ intervals that are either shorter or longer than this will result in a relatively lower rate of the avoidance response.

Although the temporal parameters of an avoidance schedule lead to systematic changes in the rate of response, the situation is not quite so clear as to the effect of shock intensity. Boren, Sidman and Herrnstein (1959) investigated this parameter. Their data suggest that over a low-shock range (up to 1 milliampere), rate of response increases with shock intensity. Above that range, response rate appears to be asymptotic with respect to shock intensity. Increases in shock intensity from 1 mA. to 3 mA. did not produce regular changes in response rates among their four experimental animals.

While rate of response may not vary reliably with certain experimental variables, the dimensions of individual response may nonetheless show systematic changes. The experiment of immediate concern involves a multiple avoidance schedule of the Sidman type. The temporal parameters (*S–S* and *R–S* intervals) remain constant in the two schedule components, but the shock intensity in each component is correlated with a specific cage illumination provided as an exteroceptive stimulus. The *S–S* and *R–S* intervals selected were those that would produce a relatively high rate of response and facilitate initial conditioning. The shock intensities chosen provided one near the bottom of the adequate range for avoidance responding (1 mA.) and the other fairly high in intensity (3 mA.).

Shock intensity (and its correlated exteroceptive stimulus) was the only respect in which the schedule components differed. The response criterion (set at threshold, 2.5 gm.) for successful avoidance was unchanged throughout the experiment. Neither schedule component directly or implicitly required a rate of response, peak force, duration, or time integral of force of response different from the other.

Method

The two-component multiple avoidance schedule was correlated with light-on (20 foot-candles at the cage floor beneath the manipulandum) or light-off. Both schedule components maintained a response-shock interval (*R–S*) of 15 seconds, and a shock-shock (*S–S*) interval of 5 seconds. Changes in the exteroceptive stimulus had no effect on these temporal parameters. All shocks were 0.30 second in duration; a Grayson-Stadler E 1064GS Shock Generator was used.

Successful conditioning was achieved with two of four animals. Both of these animals had light-off correlated with the low-intensity shock. The sequence of stimuli was as follows: 80 seconds (on), 80 (off), 40 (on), 20 (off), 20 (on), 160 (off), 10 (on), 40 (off), 160 (on), 10 (off). This basic pattern was repeated so that a day's run was some multiple of a complete cycle of 10 minutes and 20 seconds. Individual sessions were as short as two cycles for the initial stages of training and were progressively lengthened. A self-shaping procedure was attempted by simply placing the animal in the cage with all of the schedule contingencies operative. For animal 47, this procedure was effective. Animal 41 required two days of approximately 20 minutes of escape training to produce sufficient manipulandum-oriented activity to permit the schedule contingencies to maintain the response. Two animals, intended for a light-off, high-shock correlation, failed to condition to either shaping procedure. For control purposes this necessitated a light versus shock-intensity reversal stage of the experiment for the successfully conditioned animals.

The initial stage of the experiment was terminated after both animals had been exposed to the schedule for a total of approximately 25 session hours. During the last day's run of 2 hours and 4 minutes for each subject, animal 41 received 149 shocks, and animal 47 received 34 shocks.

The second stage of the experiment involved an illumination versus shock-intensity reversal. Light-off now corresponded to high-intensity shock, and light-on corresponded to low-intensity shock. Temporal parameters remained unchanged. This procedure was carried out for an additional 16 days; each daily session was 2 hours and 4 minutes in length.

Standard laboratory procedures described in Chapter 2 were observed, except that a false ceiling was placed in the cage to prevent the animals from perching on single-floor grids to avoid shock.

Results

Responses were designated on the basis of their sequential relation to the occurrence of shock in the following three classes:

1. Type A. Avoidance responses preceded by other avoidance responses without any intervening shock; this constituted the preponderant class for well-conditioned animals.

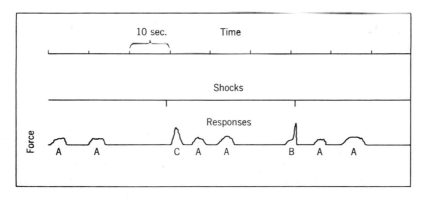

Figure 12-1   Schematic strip-chart record during Sidman-avoidance, indicating three types of response: Type A, responses preceded by other avoidance responses without any intervening shock; Type B, responses during which a shock occurred; and Type C, the first response following a shock.

2. Type B (shocked). Responses during which a shock occurred. Since avoidance (*R–S*) intervals were initiated by the termination of a response, it was possible for a response to begin before a shock was due and for the shock to occur during the course of the response.

3. Type C (postshock). The first response following shock. Type C responses occurred during *S–S* intervals; termination of Type C (as well as other) responses initiated an *R–S* interval.

The three response classes are shown schematically in Fig. 12-1.

Peak-Force Distribution During Avoidance

Avoidance (Type A) responses represent the class most remote from shock occurrence. The control, if any, exerted by the exteroceptive stimuli is least likely to be contaminated by immediate shock effects for this class of response. Figures 12-2 and 12-3 show the distributions of peak force of response for each subject during a 2-hour and 4-minute session following approximately 25 hours of prior training. The two curves in each figure represent the high-shock (S_H) and low-shock (S_L) schedule components. For both subjects S_L produced a significantly higher level of force emission than S_H.[1]

Figures 12-4 and 12-5 present comparable distributions for response duration. For both animals the distributions differ significantly; for both animals the likelihood of long response durations is greater for the low-shock (S_L) condition.

Reversal Control

Since both animals had light-on as the high-shock (S_H) schedule component, a reversal control was performed (see Method section). Figure 12-6-*A* shows the distributions of peak force of response during light-off in the initial and reversal phases of the experiment; light-on is shown in Fig. 12-6-*B*. For both stimuli the high-shock condition, whether in the initial or reversal phase, can be seen to produce somewhat lower forces than the low-shock condition. The distributions shown in Fig. 12-6, however, differ significantly only for the light-off stimulus. In light-on, the forces remained unchanged or became only slightly higher when the shock level was shifted from high to low. This control session provides reasonably good evidence that the force

---

[1] In this and all following tests that apply directly to distributions, the Kolmogorov-Smirnov two-tailed test at the 5 per cent level was applied.

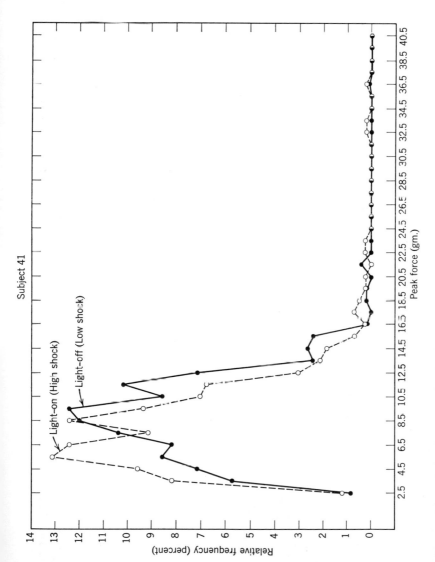

Figure 12-2 Relative frequency distributions of peak force of avoidance (Type A) responses for subject 41 during Sidman-avoidance. The distributions for light-on (high shock) and light-off (low shock) are shown separately.

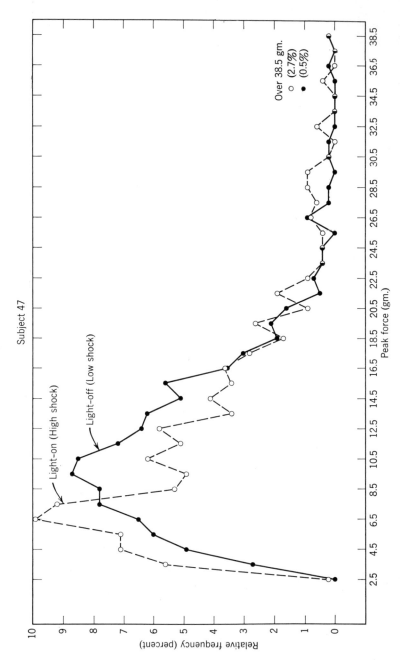

Figure 12-3 Relative frequency distributions of peak force of avoidance (Type A) responses for subject 47 during Sidman-avoidance. The distributions for light-on (high shock) and light-off (low shock) are shown separately.

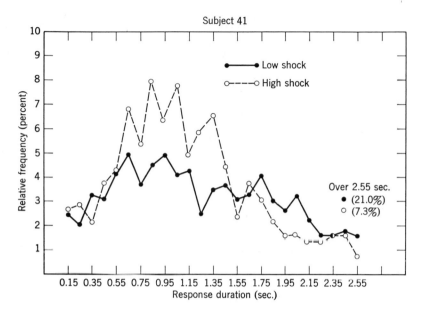

Figure 12-4 Relative frequency distributions of duration of avoidance (Type A) responses for subject 41 during Sidman-avoidance. The distributions for light-on (high shock) and light-off (low shock) are shown separately.

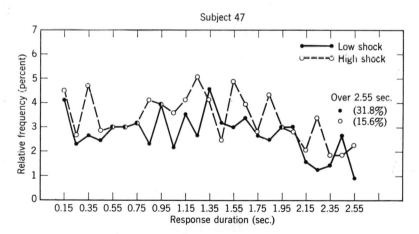

Figure 12-5 Relative frequency distributions of duration of avoidance (Type A) responses for subject 47 during Sidman-avoidance. The distributions for light-on (high shock) and light-off (low shock) are shown separately.

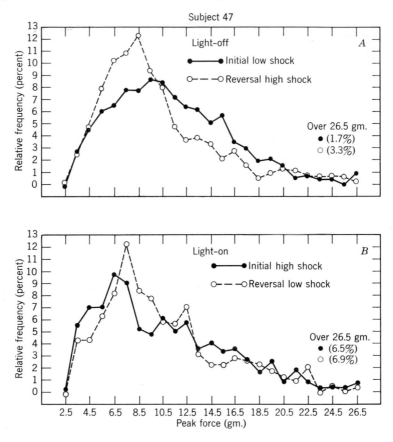

Figure 12-6 Relative frequency distributions of peak force of avoidance (Type A) responses for subject 47 during initial training and stimulus-shock reversal control phases. Light-off, correlated with low shock initially and high shock during the reversal is shown in *A*; light-on, high shock initially, low shock during reversal, is shown in *B*.

levels are primarily related to the shock intensity, although reversibility seems somewhat influenced by initial levels. The data in this regard are similar for both subjects; only animal 47 is shown.

The shift in distributions discussed for peak force of response is also evident for response duration. Figure 12-7-*A* shows a significant difference between the initial and reversal phase. The stimulus (light-off) has remained constant, but its correlated shock has been shifted from low intensity (S_L) to high intensity (S_H). For the other stimulus (light-on) the shift from high (S_H) to low (S_L) intensity shock does not

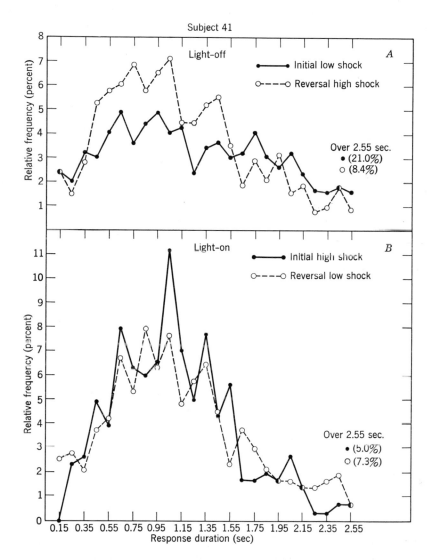

Figure 12-7 Relative frequency distributions of duration of avoidance (Type A) response for subject 41 during initial training stimulus-shock reversal control phases. Light-off, correlated with low shock initially and high shock during reversal, is shown in *A*; light-on, high shock initially, low shock during reversal, is shown in *B*.

produce a significant change in the distribution of response durations, but the trend is in the appropriate direction. Both peak force and duration of response show somewhat more peaked distributions after the extended training of the reversal phase.

Shocked and Post-Shocked Responses

The mean peak force for shocked (Type B) and postshock (Type C) responses is shown in Table 12-1. Small samples were observed since the conditioning resulted in a low frequency of shock. Comparisons based on the computed means show significant differences in the following two instances of interest: [2] shocked responses showed higher means than postshock responses; the reversal phase produced lower means of the peak-force distributions than did initial conditioning within the postshock class.

Within the shocked response class, high shock shows a higher mean peak force than does low shock; this difference, however, is not statistically significant.

TABLE 12-1

Mean Peak Force (gm.) for Shocked and Postshock Responses

	Shocked Responses (Type B)		Postshock Responses (Type C)	
	Low Shock (1 mA.)	High Shock (3 mA.)	Low Shock (1 mA.)	High Shock (3 mA.)
Initial Conditioning				
Subject 41	24.4	30.1	14.3	29.2
Subject 47	33.3	50.8	29.3	14.3
Reversal Conditioning				
Subject 41	16.5	24.6	8.5	12.3
Subject 47	37.5	68.5	25.1	7.7

[2] The two-tailed t-test appropriate to correlated scores was performed on the distribution means recorded in Table 12-1. The Ns constituting these means varied from 2 to 46. A comparison between two distributions based on the K–S test was consequently inappropriate in many instances.

TABLE 12-2

Scattergram of Peak Force and Time Since Shock Occurrence

	Peak Force (gm.)								
	0–4.9	5.0–9.9	10.0–14.9	15.0–19.9	20.0–24.9	25.0–29.9	30.0–34.9	35.0–39.9	Over 40
Over 4.80									
4.57–4.80									
4.33–4.56									
4.09–4.32									
3.85–4.08	2								
3.61–3.84									
3.37–3.60	4	1							
3.13–3.36	1								
2.89–3.12	2	2			1				
2.65–2.88	2								
2.41–2.64	6	3							
2.17–2.40	7	5							
1.93–2.16		2							
1.69–1.92									
1.45–1.68	1	1							
1.21–1.44									
0.97–1.20									
0.73–0.96		1		1					
0.49–0.72	1	2	1	2			1	1	1
0.25–0.48	1	6	5		1	2	4	1	16
0.01–0.24	1	1	1		1				1
0		3	1	1	3	2	3		5

Time Since Shock Occurrence (sec.)

The distribution of peak force of response and "time since shock occurrence" is shown in the scattergram in Table 12-2. The distribution is for animal 41, with the high- and low-intensity shock conditions combined. The data suggest that the postshock force elevation is selective to responses following shock by a brief period. The zero (0) postshock interval represents shocked responses (Type B).

Postshock response duration is significantly shorter than avoidance response duration. The means of the distributions for both subjects during the initial phase of the experiment are shown in Table 12-3. Within both classes of response for both subjects, the mean response duration for the low-shock condition is significantly greater than for the high-shock condition.

TABLE 12-3

Mean Response Duration (seconds) for Avoidance and Postshock Responses

	Avoidance Response (Type A)	Postshock Response (Type C)
Subject 41		
Low Shock (1 mA.)	1.88	0.59
High Shock (3 mA.)	1.34	0.37
Subject 47		
Low Shock (1 mA.)	2.21	0.88
High Shock (3 mA.)	1.67	0.46

Response Rate

Each schedule component constituted 50 per cent of the total running time. In the initial phase of the experiment the total number of responses for both animals was greater in the low-shock condition. After the extended training of the reversal phase both subjects showed a greater frequency of response during the high-shock condition. The mean response rates for the reversal phase are shown in Table 12-4. Assuming equal expected frequency of response, the difference is statistically significant for subject 41 and is not for subject 47 (χ^2, 5 per cent level).[3]

TABLE 12-4

Mean Response Rate, Reversal Phase

Subject	Responses/min.	
	High Shock	Low Shock
41	6.1	4.8
47	9.6	9.1

[3] Since the cage illumination in this experiment was identical with that tested for aversive properties during operant-level determinations in the experiment reported in Chapter 4 and found to be nonaversive, no additional control was deemed necessary. A further check is provided by the experiment reported in Chapter 6.

Comparison with Positive Reinforcement

The characteristics of behavior maintained with negative reinforcement in the avoidance schedule differ in several interesting respects from behavior maintained with positive reinforcement. A positive-reinforcement analog of the avoidance contingency is perhaps impossible to specify. Nevertheless, certain properties of the avoidance response differ from the properties of responses for any of the positive-reinforcement contingencies we have observed.

Two salient features of the avoidance response are the unusually long response durations and considerable regularity in the form of force emission during a single response. In CRF, with a response threshold and criterion identical to those used in the avoidance schedule (2.5-gm. F_p for both), response durations are typically well below 0.5 second (see Chapter 3), but peak-force distributions provide values similar to those of avoidance performance.[4]

The shape of the force-time record of the avoidance response shows considerable stereotypy. Samples are contained in Fig. 12-8. For comparison purposes, some samples from performance under other contingencies are provided. The gradual changes in force within a response, the absence of sharp peaks, and the small undulations were characteristic of performance for both animals during avoidance.

Avoidance Effort

Another noteworthy feature of avoidance performance is the high rate of manipulandum-oriented effort expediture (Table 12-5). The long response durations are the primary factor distinguishing the effort of the avoidance response from positively reinforced responses. Escape from the acquired aversive properties of the other behavior tends to funnel a large proportion of the total activity of the organism into the measured-response class. With a positively reinforced response, nonmeasured behavior (tray approach, pellet ingestion, etc.) tends to compete with the measured response since these aspects of behavior have also been strengthened through reinforcement.

---

[4] Early in avoidance training, response durations were frequently in excess of the system limit of 9.99 seconds. By the 25th hour, durations of this magnitude had essentially disappeared.

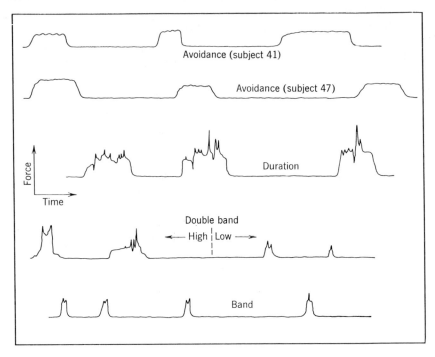

Figure 12-8 Sample strip-chart records comparing performance during avoidance for subjects 41 and 47 with that of other subjects during various positive reinforcement criteria. Response duration (1.6 sec.), double band (high, 15–20 gm., and low, 5–10 gm.), and band (8–16 gm.) are shown.

TABLE 12-5

Rate of Effort Expenditure
(gm.-sec. per minute)

(Data for CRF taken from study reported in Chapter 3)

	Avoidance	
Subject	Low Shock	High Shock
41	124.4	69.8
47	197.0	138.6
CRF		
Threshold criterion, Group I		9.5
8-gm. peak force criterion, Group III		46.5

Summary of Empirical Findings

The empirical findings are summarized below.

1. Performance within a single-schedule component (S–R, R–S, and shock-intensity constant) was as follows:

a. Peak force of response was highest when a shock occurred during a response (Type B), lower for responses immediately following shock (Type C), and lowest for the responses remote from shock occurrence (Type A).

b. The duration of response was shorter for Type C (postshock) than Type A responses.

c. The elevation in force attributable to shock occurrence appeared to diminish rapidly as a function of time following the shock.

d. Both peak force and duration of response (for all response classes) diminished in magnitude with extended training.

2. Comparisons between performances during the low-intensity (S_L) and the high-intensity (S_H) schedule components show the following:

a. Peak force of response was related directly to shock intensity for responses under the immediate control of shock (Type B, shocked responses, and Type C, postshock responses).

b. Peak force of response within Type A (responses remote from shock) was *lower* for the S_H (high shock) than the S_L (low shock).

c. The duration of response was shorter for S_H than S_L avoidance responses (Type A).

d. The rate of response was higher for S_H than S_L (after extended training).

3. Comparison with behavior maintained with positive reinforcement shows the following:

a. Peak force of response was similar in magnitude.

b. Response durations during avoidance performance were considerably longer.

c. The form of response during avoidance responding was more regular (the momentary changes in applied force were of smaller magnitude, and peaking was less sharp).

d. The rate of manipulandum-oriented effort expenditure was much greater during avoidance performance than during CRF.

As in several other experiments we have reported, the avoidance schedules produced differentiated distributions of the response dimensions in the absence of experimenter-established differentiating (or selective-reinforcement) criteria. Although the criterion for avoidance corresponded to the minimal definition of response (threshold), separate values of the response dimensions became characteristic of each shock intensity. The following three comparisons appear of particular interest: (1) performance maintained under the avoidance contingency differed from performance maintained with positive reinforcement; (2) performance under the immediate influence of shock differed from performance temporally remote from shock; (3) performance varied systematically with shock intensity.

Avoidance and Positive Reinforcement

The most noteworthy contrast between positively reinforced responding and avoidance responding concerns the duration of response. Response durations during avoidance exceeded those we found during either CRF or FR performance when an identical reinforcement criterion was involved. Although the type of reinforcement and its programming differ among the three procedures, the identical requirement in terms of the peak force, duration, or time integral of force of response necessary to meet the programmed contingencies provides one basis for comparison. For instance, in both CRF and the avoidance schedule, every single lever contact that momentarily exceeded 2.5-gm. peak force was effective as to the experimental contingency. In the FR schedule it is possible to consider two classes of contingency: a unit or step advance in the ratio cycle, and an advance to the particular cycle position or positions corresponding to pellet delivery. In all three procedures, the programmed contingency occurs upon response termination. The primary distinction among the three types of schedules is the nature of the contingency itself.

In Chapter 9 we proposed that FR schedules provide a coincidental contingency favoring responses of short duration. In that instance we took it as axiomatic that there would be a selective strengthening of those variations in behavior that systematically produced an increase in the frequency of reinforcement. It will be remembered that despite the tendency of extinction to lead to increased response duration, the FR schedules did not show a systematic increase in this dimension when compared with CRF performance.

One aspect of the experimental situation common to all positive-reinforcement contingencies is the reinforcement delivery itself. Typically, the reinforced lever press becomes a component of a behavioral chain that terminates in behavior roughly described as pellet ingestion. Here again we find a coincidental contingency that tends to

favor responses of short duration. The delay in reinforcement following lever depression is likely to be shorter when the duration of the
response itself is shorter. This may occur in escape contingencies as
well. For example, Dinsmoor, Hughes and Matsuoka (1958) found a
"press-and-release" requirement produced shorter responses than a
"press" requirement.

In the avoidance schedule the programmed consequence of each
response (initiation of a shock-delay interval) is not readily discriminable. If the reinforcement for the response is escape from the conditioned aversive properties generated by behavior other than the avoidance response, then the effective reinforcement occurs upon response
initiation itself. Then also, termination of the response reintroduces
the organism into the realm of behavior that generates the conditioned aversive properties. If the programmed contingencies called
for prolonged lever depression to continue the avoidance of shock, we
would expect eventual response durations measurable in minutes
rather than seconds (Hefferline, 1950; Winnick, 1956). However, in
the avoidance schedule we have employed, a continued lever depression in fact leads to direct punishment.

The exact circumstances of a single lever press seem best described
as a conflict situation. All varieties of nonavoidance behavior (any
behavior but lever pressing) are likely to acquire aversive properties
through correlation with shock. Escape is accomplished through lever
depression. This form of reinforcement is immediate, even though
effective avoidance is initiated by the lever-release component of the
response. Early in conditioning, long response durations led to shock
occurrence. Consequently, a single lever depression itself is likely to
become more and more aversive with a passage of time. Escape now
corresponds to termination of the response. The situation is not unlike the classic avoidance-avoidance conflict. In this instance the two
aversive stimuli are produced by behavior. First, the aversiveness of
nonresponse increases the probability of response persistence; second,
the aversiveness of response persistence increases the likelihood of response termination. In addition to these properties that are produced
by the schedule contingencies, it is likely that the effort of responding
itself produces unconditioned aversive properties (Hull, 1943; Keller
and Schoenfeld, 1950) and that the release component of the bar press
is a necessary link in the chain of behavior leading to subsequent bar
pressing.

For positively reinforced responses, conflict is essentially absent
during the course of a single lever depression. The release component

of the response systematically initiates the exteroceptive-stimulus concomitants of pellet delivery. Although the release component of avoidance response also initiates the scheduled contingency, the operation has no exteroceptive-stimulus correlates. If it had (and this can be experimentally tested, for example, by initiation of a "safe" signal), response durations during avoidance would probably be more like those of CRF performance. The decline of response durations with progressive training during avoidance suggests that the temporal aspects of the contingency were taking some measure of control. In the absence of exteroceptive stimuli, certain components of the organism's own behavior may have provided the basis for closer approximation of the minimum requirements of the schedule.

The undulations that were observed in the force-time records of individual responses (Fig. 12-8) may be a behavioral manifestation of the conflict status of the response. The tendency to release the lever accompanies a tendency to continue the lever press, producing a kind of oscillation in the behavior. Oscillation of this sort is frequently observed in runway conflict experiments and has been noted for the free operant (Winnick, 1956).

Although positive-reinforcement and avoidance contingencies appear to differ in the way they selectively strengthen particular values of response duration, they do not differ in their effect on peak force of response. Extremely low levels of force emission will tend to undergo extinction in both kinds of contingencies, since failure to reach response threshold corresponds to ineffectual behavior.

With CRF, the conditions for learning close conformity to the minimum force requirement are perhaps optimized. The feedback from a particular level of force emission precedes reinforcement or nonreinforcement by a short period of time. Consequently, discrimination of the adequate force level is likely. With avoidance, the reinforcement (secondary) presumably occurs upon response emission. Even when the force level is below that required for avoidance, some reinforcement presumably occurs. The failure of the behavior to initiate an avoidance interval may not be discriminable to the subject for several seconds (when the next shock occurs), or may be totally obscured (when a subsequent response occurs before a shock is due). The difficulty in avoidance is that the immediate reinforcement for any individual response is mediated by the subject's own behavior.

As our results have shown, after extended avoidance training the peak force of response came in closer approximation to the minimum requirement of the 2.5-gm. threshold. After 25 hours of exposure to the schedule, changes were still taking place. Under CRF (Chapter 3) peak-force distributions reach a stable limit in a relatively short period of time. The difference in performance may well be attributable to the difference in the adequacy of the exteroceptive stimuli as a basis for discrimination of the minimum force requirement. Like the avoidance performance, FR performance frequently does not produce any immediate exteroceptive reinforcement for individual responses. In FR (Chapter 9) it appeared likely that a relatively high level of force emission would continue for responses in the cycle positions that were temporally remote from antecedent reinforcement.

Direct Effects of Shock

The disparity in the response dimensions between the general class of avoidance responses (Type A) and those immediately following shock (Type B) is comparable with certain peculiarities that have been observed in the rate of response (Sidman, 1958). Sidman notes that closely spaced responses ("bursts") are frequently initiated by the response following shock occurrence. In accord with his contention that the spacing of response is a discriminative phenomenon, he suggests that the "bursts" reflect a temporary broadening of the generalization gradient.

Immediately following shock, high peak forces of response occur. If we consider force emission as a discriminative process, the broadening of generalization gradient is again indicated. The basis for such an effect remains a matter of conjecture. It is possible that shock introduces some disruptive factor into the neurological or muscular functioning of the organism. Numerous unconditioned effects of shock are well known. We have observed high peak forces and abrupt response terminations when shock occurs during a response. These aspects of the behavior appear directly attributable to unconditioned responses related to shock.

The immediate effects of shock that were observed appear to dissipate rapidly as a function of time. Beyond approximately two seconds after shock, the level of force emission was similar to that for avoidance responses remote from shock. The short time course of the effect of shock suggests that some unconditioned behavior directly related to the shock mediates the peak-force and duration changes that occur for the responses within this postshock time interval.

Effects of Shock Intensity and Correlated Stimuli

In considering the effects of shock intensity upon the avoidance behavior, one must distinguish between those effects that are immediately related to shock occurrence and those that relate to the exteroceptive stimulus correlated with a particular level of shock.

We have suggested that the immediate effects of shock on the conditioned response relate to, or are mediated by, unconditioned responses elicited by shock itself. Peak force of Type B response is elevated in magnitude in direct proportion to shock intensity. This relationship is in accord with certain general characteristics of respondent behavior: the magnitude of the unconditioned response relates directly to the magnitude of the unconditioned stimulus. Although the lever press itself is not respondent behavior, there can be little doubt that the musculature used in this response (and consequently the dimensions of response) will show the effect of unconditioned responses to the shock.

The inverse relation between the magnitude of the peak force of Type A responses and the cue for the shock intensity avoided requires a different explanation. When responses do not immediately follow shock, the high-shock intensity cue occasions a lower level of peak-force emission than the low-shock intensity stimulus.

A restatement of the effect may cast a different light on the phenomenon. It might be said that avoidance responses for high-intensity shock more closely approximate the minimum criterion for avoidance. As we have emphasized, response magnitude per se is not an appropriate measure of strength for a conditioned operant. A more appropriate measure might in fact be some index of response conformity to experimental requirements. In this sense, the high-intensity shock produces greater response strength than the low-intensity shock.

Closer conformity to the experimental contingencies, with progressive training, frequently appears in operant-conditioning procedures. When we have differentially reinforced particular response variations, progressive training has typically increased the likelihood that individual responses will meet the criterion. The levels of peak force, duration, or integral of force of response may increase or decrease, depending on the direction of change that increases conformity to the experimental requirements. An effect of this sort is also apparent with rate of response. In schedules of intermittent reinforcement, discrimination training, etc., the organism tends to optimize reinforcement. Imperfection, however, typically appears in the final level of performance since the behavioral output of the organism frequently exceeds the minimal requirements of the experimental procedure. To cite a few examples—fixed-interval schedules produce more than just a single response at the moment reinforcement is due; avoidance schedules produce responses in excess of the minimum requirement for avoidance; and "band" reinforcement produces force levels above and below the bands. The inefficiency of the behavior is generally attributed to the inability of the organism to discriminate the contingency. When the behavior closely approximates the minimum contingency requirements, variability may decrease the likelihood of reinforcement. For instance, when an interval schedule of reinforcement contains only a brief period of reinforcement eligibility, the likelihood that a response will occur within the interval increases with an increase in the rate of response.

Given the opportunity, the organism will learn to emit the most biologically conservative mode of behavior consistent with reinforcement. Generally, this "conservativism" implies emitting the fewest responses of smallest magnitude appropriate to the reinforcement history of the organism. Reinforcement of effective, but not the most conservative, variations in behavior will lead to the recurrence of these forms of behavior. The degree to which stimuli are available to cue the various aspects of behavior will determine the rapidity with which the most conservative mode of performance will be approached and a stable level of performance maintained. The learning also depends upon the reinforcement quantity, frequency, and temporal proximity to the response and its antecedent stimulus complex.

In the absence of exteroceptive stimuli that are experimentally related to reinforcement, the organism's own behavior (feedback) may acquire the appropriate discriminative control of subsequent behavior and, as with avoidance, the behavior itself may mediate reinforcement for the measured response.

The degree to which the organism exceeds the minimum reinforcement requirements may be attributable in large measure to generalization. Generalization undoubtedly is based in part upon an inherent limit to sensory capacities. The performance under a particular experimental procedure probably reflects this limit to some extent. Typically, variations from optimum performance *do* receive reinforcement; closer approximation frequently leads to a reduction in reinforcement. Under such circumstances, the biologically conservative mode of performance seems to be at some level sufficiently above the minimum to make failure to meet the criterion unlikely.

Amount of Reinforcement in Avoidance

As to positively reinforced behavior, we have demonstrated that the amount of reinforcement received is an effective variable (Chapter 10). Amount of reinforcement was shown to produce inverse changes in peak force of response. It is possible that the two levels of shock intensity in the avoidance schedule constitute two distinct *amounts* of reinforcement in the two different schedule components. Experimental requirements are established for both the temporal distribution of response and the dimensional properties of individual responses. In order for reinforcement to take place the subject must learn what to do and when to do it. Both "what" and "when" are discriminative phenomena. The evidence we have produced suggests that the role of reinforcement in such acquisition cannot be treated in a simple yes-no manner, particularly as it affects the dimensional properties of individual responses.

It is possible to consider the amount of reinforcement for an individual avoidance response as being directly related to the shock intensity avoided. The avoidance of very weak shocks, for instance, may provide too little reinforcement to maintain the behavior. It can be assumed that the light correlated with high-intensity shock will elicit respondent behavior differing at least in magnitude from respondent behavior elicited by the light that has been correlated with low-intensity shock. Following the similar hypotheses of Schoenfeld (1950b) and Mowrer (1939), it may be said that the organism escapes from a more aversive stimulus or undergoes greater fear reduction for those responses occurring in the presence of the light correlated with the high-intensity shock.

The difference between the high-shock and low-shock avoidance behavior was like the difference between the performance later in training (at the end of the reversal phase) and the performance earlier in training (at the end of the initial phase). Both high shock and more training produced lower peak force.

Our findings for response duration were similar to those for the peak force of response. This similarity might merely reflect the positive correlation between peak force and duration described in Chapter 3. However, shorter response durations in the high-shock component of the schedule might also be considered performance in relatively closer conformity to the minimum schedule requirements.

It is possible that the low peak forces and short durations of response in the high-shock schedule component relate to the occasional direct punishment of responses. Earlier in this discussion we proposed a conflict status for any single response. Since shock may occur during a response, the subjects acquire a tendency to terminate the response. The conditioned aversiveness of response emission would probably relate to the shock intensity. When a light is paired with a high-intensity shock, it may lead to the generation of more aversive properties of response emission itself. Consequently, the tendency to escape may be greater. This tendency could be reflected by shorter response durations and lower peak forces, since lower values of each measure imply smaller magnitudes of the feedback components of response emission. During training, the longer the duration of response emission (and the more the feedback components of this behavior), the more likely it was that the animal was shocked while responding.

It is unlikely that the observed differences in performance were attributable to an unconditioned effect of the light intensity. In addition to our control constituting the reversal phase of the avoidance experiment, we have used lights of the same intensity in several other experiments without observing any unconditioned effects related to intensity (see footnote p. 248).

The rate of response at the end of the reversal phase of the experiment was higher for the high-shock than for the low-shock condition, contrary to the relative response rates earlier in training. At the end of the reversal phase, both animals received fewer high- than low-intensity shocks. Boren, Sidman and Herrnstein (1959) presented data showing a systematic decrease in the number of shocks received with an increase in shock intensity. This measure (conformity to the contingency) might be interpreted as positive evidence for greater response strength with greater intensity of the controlling shock.

A difficulty in the analysis of many operant experimental results has been that a greater behavioral output, by fortuitous circumstance, has constituted better performance. Particularly with the dimensional aspects of individual responses, greater output is not necessarily better performance. In the avoidance experiment we have demonstrated that the higher level of shock will produce more effective avoidance with less superfluous behavior (lower peak forces and shorter durations of response). We have suggested that this difference in performance may be attributable to the greater reinforcing effect of escape from the more aversive stimulus. Such effects as the acquisition of shorter escape latencies with higher shock intensities have been reported (Possey, 1948). These effects may also be interpreted as a superior mode of performance attributable to greater reinforcement. With the avoidance response we have followed the hypothesis that the reinforcement for an individual response is escape from acquired aversive stimuli. These aversive properties have their origin in the pairing of certain forms of behavior with shock occurrence. Extending this argument, we suggest that the degree of acquired aversiveness relates to the shock intensity and that ultimately the discriminative learning will relate to the effective reinforcement for the behavior.

Chapter Thirteen

General Considerations

MENSURATIVE PROPERTIES of responses have been discussed without any claim to comprehensiveness. We have sought to concentrate our efforts on an examination of behavioral processes that are either presumably well known by virtue of previous "frequency-of-response" research or relatively unknown because of previous technique limitations. The presumably well-known processes are exemplified by the experiments dealing with fixed-ratio and fixed-interval schedules of reinforcement; the relatively unknown processes are illustrated by the work on force-proportional reinforcement. In choosing this approach to the diverse research problems presenting themselves, we hoped to select areas that would provide the behavioral scientist with information whereby he could evaluate the importance of the measurement procedures here employed—in terms of supplementing existing descriptions of behavior or of examining phenomena heretofore undescribed. Before closing this account, we think it appropriate for us to comment on several general considerations concerning issues that the reflective reader will have perceived as central to the research reported in the foregoing pages.

Measurement versus Counting Operations. Neither of the authors can represent himself as a student of the philosophy of measurement. The remarks in this section concern only certain empirical considerations that we believe are important in an analysis of operant behavior.

Foremost among these is the counting-operation procedure that permits the scientist to set aside the problems of measuring individual responses in favor of examining the effects of these responses on the environment (for instance, number of closures of a microswitch) or of determining the time between successive occurrences of these events. In the time determination, it can be argued that measurement is, indeed, taking place; however, this measurement operation is not concerned with the properties of responses themselves but with the passage of time between responses. And as noted elsewhere (Chapter 1), "time between responses" thus becomes an index of bar-pressing behavior relative to the strength of other ongoing behavior.

In this sense, one cannot help wondering why the criticism offered by Skinner of "choice-point" behavior as an analytic instrument does not apply as well to "frequency-of-response" (or "time-between-responses") procedures. He said: "Instead of *measuring behavior directly*, Tolman is reduced to determining a 'behavior ratio' . . ." (Skinner, 1938, p. 437; italics ours). Surely, if direct measurement of behavior is desirable, it is more closely approximated by operations that examine the mensurative characteristics of responses per se than by "choice between responses"—regardless of whether the choice is expressed as "time between responses" (choice between pressing and not pressing the bar) or as probabilities in a T-maze (choice between left turn and right turn).

Response Properties versus Response Occurrence. On the other hand, we do not mean to imply that direct measurement is of necessity inherently superior to indirect measurement. Fundamental to the consideration of the analytic importance of measurement versus counting operations is the question of what it is about behavior that the scientist wishes to describe. Confining our remarks to operant behavior, the answer is that the scientist seeks to describe modifications in the behavioral repertoire of the organism as it interacts with the environment, particularly as a function of reinforcement and drive operations. Observation tells us that there are two principal means of organism interaction with the world about it: emission of responses with greater or lesser frequency, as demanded by the contingencies required for reinforcement; variations in the characteristics of individual responses, again as reinforcement contingencies dictate. However, this dichotomy is largely of descriptive convenience, inasmuch as the organism typically encounters an environment in which both types of behavioral modification have utility. As has been previously noted (p. 3), even routine bar pressing requires a minimum magnitude of response for lever depression; by the same token, "band-discrimination" procedures (Chapters 5, 6) indirectly place a premium upon rapid as well as accurate responding. In addition, an inevitable concomitant of both these forms of behavioral interaction with the environment is exchange of energy. As we observed in Chapter 1, the nature of our physical world is such that operant behavior cannot occur without the exertion of finite forces over finite durations. But unless the experimenter deliberately creates a situation in which reinforcement is contingent upon specific effort criteria, the characteristics of a law (if any) between effort demanded and effort expended remain a matter for conjecture. It is hoped that the constant-effort and fixed-effort schedules described in Chapter 8 represent a step toward experimental analysis of effort. But we must make explicit our own view that the biological organism is more a "discriminative machine" than a "work machine." In other words, reinforcement contingencies give rise to behavior that can be understood better in terms of discrimination processes than in terms of effort relations. And yet effort relations influence discriminative processes in at least two ways. First, the organism tends to achieve some balance between what its discriminative capacities permit in the way of quality of performance and the level of effort required to maintain this proficiency (see Chapter 3). Second, the exertion of effort may by itself provide feedback cues that facilitate the development of discrimination (see Chapter 9).

We do not yet know how important these considerations are to the formulation of principles of behavior. It seems to us, however, that the required analyses must include detailed examination of individual response characteristics as well as the more conventional "rate-of-emission" dependent variables.

Strength of Conditioned Response. We hope we have indicated that we do not equate force (or magnitude) of conditioned response with strength of conditioned response. If by strength the scientist implies some index of the extent to which a particular habit has been learned, then neither force nor frequency of response bears a simple, direct, monotonic relation to strength. The relation between either force or frequency and response strength depends on the task criteria established by the experimenter, and how well the subject has come to meet them. In FR schedules, rate of response is directly indicative of strength; in FI schedules, an inverse relation obtains. Similarly, depending on the requirements of the reinforcement contingency (or "criterion," as we have used the term), force of response could be either positively or negatively correlated with strength as herein defined.

Perhaps our emphasis in several analyses upon "number of responses reaching criterion" serves to call attention to the usefulness of separating response "threshold" from reinforcement "criterion," with its attendant implication that "proportion of criterion responses" is a suitable index for conditioned-response strength.

Feedback and the Nature of Operant Responding. Ever since the formulation of the Heisenberg Principle, it has become commonplace to observe that the conclusions obtained from an experimental program, as well as the scientific laws resulting therefrom, are shaped by the laboratory techniques used by the researcher. And so it is with bar-pressing behavior. In the conventional situation, the use of a microswitch to record responses indirectly gives rise to the view that the experimental organism behaves as if it were a switch. What originated as a counting convenience becomes an implied characteristic of the organism.

The conception of lever-pressing behavior thus tends to take its form from the microswitch; accordingly, the response is conceived of as being "ballistic," "open loop," and nondimensional in nature. The research here reported leads us to conjecture otherwise; we surmise that the response, rather than being ballistic, is regulated by feedback and is therefore closed loop rather than open loop.

Evidence supporting our view comes from the many frequency distributions presented in the foregoing pages, particularly those that show the influence of reinforcement criteria upon the mensurative properties of response. The consequences of pharmacological interruption of cutaneous loops, described in Chapter 7, provide additional support for the "closed-loop" model of response.

Is the difference in conception of response of any systematic importance? Again, we do not yet know. However, the type of analysis represented by what Skinner long ago termed the "double-discrimination" problem (Skinner, 1938) and that we hope we carried a step forward in the research reported in Chapter 6, seems necessary to a fuller understanding of the processes underlying continuity of behavior (or "chaining") and the relations between differentiation and discrimination (Chapter 4). The relative neglect of studies bearing on the role of cutaneous and kinesthetic cues originating in the organism's own behavior may relate more to technical limitations and conceptual restrictions (for instance, the "ballistic" nature of bar pressing) than to the inherent realities of behavior.

Relation of Research to Skinner and Hull. Despite our comments concerning the limitations of counting procedures, there is no question that our research rests on the prior labors of Skinner and his associates. We see our work, at most, as possibly extending or supplementing the conventional Skinnerian approach to the analysis of behavior. It seems to us that the nature of the extension—should it indeed prove to be one—could bring bar-pressing technique closer to the Hullian tradition as a result of our emphasis on force and effort of response and the consequent implications for the "inhibition" construct (see Chapter 1 and pp. 162, 253). Because our own backgrounds have been principally Skinnerian, we have not commented as much as perhaps the data warrant on the relation of our findings to Hull's system. We trust that this inadequacy will be removed eventually by our more Hullian-oriented colleagues!

References

Amsel, A. The role of frustrative nonreward in non-continuous reward situations. *Psychol. Bull.*, 1958, **55**, 102–119.

Anger, D. The dependence of interresponse times upon the relative reinforcement of different interresponse times. *J. exp. Psychol.*, 1956, **52**, 145–161.

Anger, D. The role of temporal discrimination in the reinforcement of Sidman avoidance behavior. *J. exp. Anal. Behav.*, 1963, **6**, 477–506.

Antonitis, J. J. Response variability in the white rat during conditioning, extinction, and reconditioning. *J. exp. Psychol.*, 1951, **42**, 273–281.

Bass, M. J., & Hull, C. L. The irradiation of a tactile conditioned reflex in man. *J. comp. Psychol.*, 1934, **17**, 47–65.

Belyakov, V. V. Contributions to the physiology of differentiation of external stimuli. Thesis, 1911. Cited by I. P. Pavlov, *Conditioned reflexes.* (Translated by G. V. Anrep.) London: Oxford Univer. Press, 1927.

Block, A. H. Some relations between stimulus discrimination and response differentiation. Unpublished doctoral dissertation, Princeton Univer., 1960.

Blough, D. S. Delayed matching in the pigeon. *J. exp. Anal. Behav.*, 1959, **2**, 151–160.

Boren, J. J., Sidman, M., & Herrnstein, R. J. Avoidance, escape, and extinction as a function of shock intensity. *J. comp. physiol. Psychol.*, 1959, **52**, 420–425.

Boren, J. J. Resistance to extinction as a function of the fixed ratio. *J. exp. Psychol.*, 1961, **61**, 304–308.

Cannon, W. B., & Washburn, A. L. An explanation of hunger. *Amer. J. Physiol.*, 1912, **29**, 441–454.

Catania, A. C. Concurrent performances, reinforcement interaction, and response independence. *J. exp. Anal. Behav.*, 1963, **6**, 253–263.

Clark, R. Some time-correlated reinforcement schedules and their effects on behavior. *J. exp. Anal. Behav.*, 1959, **2**, 1–22.

Crespi, L. P. Quantitative variation of incentive and performance in the white rat. *Amer. J. Psychol.*, 1942, **55**, 467–517.

Di Lollo, V. Studies of the Crespi effect. Unpublished doctoral dissertation, The Univer. of Western Australia, 1962.

Di Lollo, V., Ensminger, W. D., & Notterman, J. M. Response force as a function of amount of reinforcement. *J. exp. Psychol.*, 1965, **70**, 27–31.

Dinsmoor, J. A., Hughes, L. H., & Matsuoka, Y. Escape-from-shock training in a free-response situation. *Amer. J. Psychol.*, 1958, **71**, 325–337.

Estes, W. K. Stimulus-response theory of drive. In M. R. Jones (Ed.), *Nebraska symposium on motivation*. Lincoln: Univer. of Nebraska Press, 1958. Pp. 35–69.

Ferster, C. B., & Skinner, B. F. *Schedules of reinforcement*. New York: Appleton-Century-Crofts, 1957.

Frick, F. C. An analysis of an operant discrimination. *J. Psychol.*, 1948, **26**, 93–123.

Goldberg, I. A. Relations of response variability in conditioning and extinction. Unpublished doctoral dissertation, Columbia Univer., 1959.

Halasz, M. F. Emotional response to nonreinforcement. (ltr.) *Science*, 1963, **139**, 1128–1129.

Hearst, E. The behavioral effects of some temporally defined schedules of reinforcement. *J. exp. Anal. Behav.*, 1958, **1**, 45–55.

Hebb, D. O. Drives and the C. N. S. (Conceptual Nervous System). *Psychol. Rev.*, 1955, **62**, 243–254.

Hefferline, R. F. An experimental study of avoidance. *Genet. Psychol. Mongr.*, 1950, **42**, 231–334.

Hodgman, C. D. (Ed.) *Handbook of chemistry and physics*. (27th ed.) Cleveland: Chemical Rubber Publishing, 1943.

Hovland, C. I. The generalization of conditioned responses. I. The sensory generalization of conditioned responses with varying frequencies of tone. *J. gen. Psychol.*, 1937, **17**, 125–148.

Hull, C. L. *Principles of behavior*. New York: Appleton-Century-Crofts, 1943.

Hull, C. L. *Essentials of behavior*. New Haven: Yale Univer. Press, 1951.

Keller, F. S., & Schoenfeld, W. N. *Principles of psychology*. New York: Appleton-Century-Crofts, 1950.

Kimble, G. A. *Hilgard and Marquis' conditioning and learning*. (2nd ed.) New York: Appleton-Century-Crofts, 1961.

King, R. A. The effects of training and motivation on the components of a learned instrumental response. Unpublished doctoral dissertation, Duke Univer., 1959.

Kleiner, I. S. *Human biochemistry*. (2nd ed.) St. Louis: C. V. Mosby, 1948.

Lashley, K. S., & Wade, M. The Pavlovian theory of generalization. *Psychol. Rev.*, 1946, **53**, 72–87.

Margulies, S. Response duration in operant level, regular reinforcement, and extinction. *J. exp. Anal. Behav.*, 1961, **4**, 317–321.

Marton, T. Peripheral afferent cutaneous information and the control of voluntary motor activity. Unpublished doctoral dissertation, Princeton Univer., 1962.

Mechner, F. Probability relations within response sequences under ratio reinforcement. *J. exp. Anal. Behav.*, 1958, **1**, 109–121.

Millenson, J. R., & Hurwitz, H. M. B. Some temporal and structural properties of behavior during conditioning and extinction. *J. exp. Anal. Behav.*, 1961, **4**, 97–106.

Millenson, J. R., Hurwitz, H. M. B., & Nixon, W. L. B. Influence of reinforcement schedules on response duration. *J. exp. Anal. Behav.*, 1961, **4**, 243–250.

Miller, N. E. Learnable drives and rewards. In S. S. Stevens (Ed.), *Handbook of experimental psychology*. New York: Wiley, 1951.

Mintz, D. E. Force of response during ratio reinforcement. *Science*, 1962, **138**, 516–517.

Mintz, D. E. Emotional response to nonreinforcement. (reply to Halasz' ltr.) *Science*, 1963, **139**, 1129.

Morfield, M. A. A fixed effort schedule of reinforcement. Unpublished master's thesis, Princeton Univer., 1963.

Mowrer, O. H. A stimulus-response analysis of anxiety and its role as a reinforcing agent. *Psychol. Rev.*, 1939, **46**, 553–566.

Mowrer, O. H. *Learning theory and behavior*. New York: Wiley, 1960.

Notterman, J. M. A study of some relations among aperiodic reinforcement, discrimination training, and secondary reinforcement. *J. exp. Psychol.*, 1951, **41**, 161–169.

Notterman, J. M. Force emission during bar pressing. *J. exp. Psychol.*, 1959, **58**, 341–347.

Notterman, J. M., & Block, A. H. Response differentiation during a simple discrimination. *J. exp. Anal. Behav.*, 1960, **3**, 289–291.

Notterman, J. M., & Mintz, D. E. Exteroceptive cueing of response force. *Science*, 1962, **135**, 1070–1071.

Pavlov, I. P. *Conditioned reflexes*. (Translated by G. V. Anrep.) London: Oxford Univer. Press, 1927.

Possey, G. E. The influence of intensity of unconditioned stimulus upon acquisition of a conditioned response. *J. exp. Psychol.*, 1948, **38**, 120 128.

Razran, G. Stimulus generalization of conditioned responses. *Psychol. Bull.*, 1949, **46**, 337–365.

Reynolds, B. Acquisition of a simple spatial discrimination as a function of the amount of reinforcement. *J. exp. Psychol.*, 1950, **40**, 152–160.

Reynolds, G. S. Relativity of response rate and reinforcement frequency in a multiple schedule. *J. exp. Anal. Behav.*, 1961a, **4**, 179–184.

Reynolds, G. S. Contrast, generalization, and the process of discrimination. *J. exp. Anal. Behav.*, 1961b, **4**, 289–294.

Shaefer, H., & Steinhorst, R. The effect of changing the schedule of reinforcement upon duration of responding. *J. exp. Anal. Behav.*, 1959, **2**, 335–342.

Schoenfeld, W. N. On the difference in resistance to extinction following regular and periodic reinforcement. *Notes, Conference on the Experimental Analysis of Behavior*. (mimeographed, issued from Indiana Univer.), 1950a, No. 20.

Schoenfeld, W. N. An experimental approach to anxiety, escape, and avoidance behavior. In P. H. Hoch, & J. Zubin (Eds.), *Anxiety*. New York: Grune & Stratton, 1950b.

Schoenfeld, W. N., Cumming, W. W., & Hearst, E. On the classification of reinforcement schedules. *Proc. Nat. Acad. Sci.*, 1956, **42**, 563–570.

Sidman, M. Avoidance conditioning with brief shock and no exteroceptive warning signal. *Science*, 1953a, **118**, 157–158.

Sidman, M. Two temporal parameters of the maintenance of avoidance behavior by the white rat. *J. comp. physiol. Psychol.*, 1953b, **46**, 253–261.

Sidman, M. Some notes on "bursts" in free-operant avoidance experiments. *J. exp. Anal. Behav.*, 1958, **1**, 167–172.

Skinner, B. F. *The behavior of organisms: an experimental analysis*. New York: Appleton-Century, 1938.

Skinner, B. F. Are theories of learning necessary? *Psychol. Rev.*, 1950, **57**, 193–216.

Smith, M., & Duffy, M. Evidence for dual reinforcing effect of sugar. *J. comp. physiol. Psychol.*, 1957, **50**, 242–247.

Sollman, T. *A manual of pharmacology.* (8th ed.) Philadelphia: Saunders, 1957.

Solomon, R. L. The influence of work on behavior. *Psychol. Bull.,* 1948, **45,** 1–40.

Spence, K. W. The differential response in animals to stimuli varying within a single dimension. *Psychol. Rev.,* 1937, **44,** 430–444.

Sperry, R. W. Functional results of crossing sensory nerves in the rat. *J. comp. Neurol.,* 1943, **78,** 59–90.

Trotter, J. R. The physical properties of bar pressing behavior and the problem of reactive inhibition. *Quart. J. exp. Psychol.,* 1956, **8,** 97–106.

Winnick, Wilma. Anxiety indicators in an avoidance response during conflict and nonconflict. *J. comp. physiol. Psychol.,* 1956, **49,** 52–59.

Woodworth, R. S., & Schlosberg, H. *Experimental psychology.* New York: Holt, 1954.

Zeaman, D. Response latency as a function of the amount of reinforcement. *J. exp. Psychol.,* 1949, **39,** 466–483.

Index